the
Freedom Companion
for stopping hair pulling

Annette Pasternak, Ph.D.

Published by Tula Vayu in 2017

First edition; First printing

Design and writing © 2017 Annette Pasternak

StopSkinPickingCoach.com

ISBN 978-0-9912347-4-5

Introduction to the Freedom Companion
(why you need this book)

Becoming free from chronic compulsive hair pulling is challenging, to say the least. The Freedom Companion is designed to make it easier and to make your efforts more effective.

From my own experience becoming free of a similar body-focused repetitive behavior (BFRB), skin picking, and in my nearly five years of experience coaching others to stop skin picking and hair pulling, I have clarified what you need to succeed at it, and I have designed the Freedom Companion to help you fulfill those needs and experience long-term recovery from hair pulling.

Here's the big one:

You need to focus on the positive, not the pulling.

Rather than trying to break a negative habit, you need to create new *positive habits* that have the effect of interrupting and / or otherwise diminishing the *undesired* habit.

So you need to keep your attention on the task of creating positive action habits, and the Freedom Companion will help you do that.

When I say you need to focus on the positive, I'm not only referring to positive actions, but also to a positive outlook, mood and attitude. A person who is overall happy and looking at the process of reducing their pulling in a positive way is going to be much more successful at it than one who is depressed and hopeless, because they will be taking positive action aligned with their hopes for a different and better future than what they are currently experiencing.

I understand that a hair pulling problem, especially if it's been with you a long time, comes with a large amount and variety of negative emotions – hopelessness, self-doubt, shame and anger directed towards yourself for doing it. But I want you to understand that those feelings are holding you back, and you need to be able to release them and cultivate positive emotions. It is not your fault that you have a hair pulling problem. Although you cannot control it by willing yourself to "just stop" doing it, I know you *can* learn how to get past it.

And since part of that journey is increasing the amount of positive emotions you feel, the Freedom Companion will help you do that.

You don't ever have to be 100% hopeful and doubt-free, but you do need to cultivate the hope you do have so it grows. It will also help you to learn to look more on the sunny side of things. Those of us with BFRBs tend to focus more on the imperfection, on what's wrong rather than what's right, and we need practice to focus more on the positive.

The Freedom Companion will help you use positive psychology techniques to increase your mood and overall mental positivity. When we think and feel positive, we naturally gravitate toward positive actions.

Reading an encouraging inspiring quote, writing something you're grateful for and writing an affirmation (something you wish was true about yourself that you want to encourage with your own words) will start your day off on a positive note.

Consistency of positive actions is key

As there are many similarities between compulsive hair pulling and skin picking, and they respond to the same methods, I recommend that you use my book, "Skin Picking: The Freedom to Finally Stop" to help you increase your awareness, identify the patterns of your pulling and determine what strategic actions and lifestyle changes you can take to intervene. You will also find helpful articles about hair pulling on the website bfrb.org. After you have figured out which strategies to implement and what lifestyle changes to make, the only thing that's hard is getting yourself to remember to do them consistently.

That's not trivial though. It's something most of us struggle with. The Freedom Companion is designed to help you remember to take consistent action and to make these helpful actions habits.

In order to become free of hair pulling long-term, you need to take action consistently and often. A few rounds of 4-8-8 breathing (learn how in my free Freedom Kit at stopskinpickingcoach.com) won't make a big difference if you only remember to do it once every week or two. It will make a huge difference if you do it consistently three or five times a day.

You want to feel good about the work you're doing, the positive steps you're taking. Acknowledging yourself for taking actions during the day, by checking them off each evening, will make you feel good about yourself and your efforts and will encourage more of them.

If you do something one day, especially if you notice it has a positive effect, you'll be more likely to remember to do it again the next day.

Ultimately, what you want is to make certain actions habits. Which ones? The tools, tricks and self-care strategies that move the needle for you in the way of reducing your pulling. Once something is a habit, it takes no energy to do. On the other hand, when the question of doing that thing or not is a fresh decision you have to make every day, it drains your willpower and decision-making ability, every day. Making new positive habits puts your helpful strategies on automatic so they *will* help you every day, almost effortlessly.

You may have heard the often-repeated, "it takes 21 days to make a habit". Unfortunately, research has shown us that is not true. It actually takes an average of (depending on the habit) 66 days. The Freedom Companion will help you make new positive habits, provided that **the first positive habit you make is to use the Freedom Companion every day.**

How to use the Freedom Companion

Ideally you will use the daily pages of the Freedom Companion in this way: Start your morning by reading the inspirational quote and writing your gratitude and affirmation for the day. Return to the log in the evening to check off your positive actions, record your mood, calmness, energy level and pulling, etc. Then review your page and your day and see what you learn.

I recommend that you keep your Freedom Companion on your nightstand and make it a habit to use it first thing when you wake up and also last thing before you go to sleep. How do you ensure that you make it a habit? Ask yourself, "what is the most important step I can take right now to ensure that I use my Freedom Companion every day?" Whatever answer you come up with, take action on it now. Perhaps that is setting an alarm or reminder on your phone to remind you each day, twice a day to do your Freedom Companion. Do it now. You may also want to visualize yourself being about to turn off the light at night when you notice your Freedom Companion and reach for it instead.

The Daily Pages

Here is the breakdown of the different parts of the daily pages and the purpose of each.

Inspiring Quote:

We are a product of the thoughts we have in our minds as a result of the thoughts we surround ourselves with (other people's words). Are most people around you positive or negative? Talking about possibilities or complaining? Inspiring or dragging you down? The quote of the day is a little infusion of positivity and encouragement or humor at the start of the day. Just that little thought of another person we don't even know can really affect us. On the days I was reading and selecting positive quotes and inserting them into the Freedom Companion Daily Pages, I noticed feeling especially happy and energetic.

Mood, calmness, energy level, pulling:

These you can all record on a 0-10 scale. 10 is the most positive rating.

(There are also other options for recording pulling, discussed below.)

Your mood – This is a rating of the overall quality of your emotions that day - positive versus negative. Were you feeling happy and other positive emotions for the entirety of the day? That would be a 10. Or were you the most depressed, grouchy, negative-feeling version of yourself? You would rate that a 0. Most likely you were somewhere in between, so quickly decide on a number that you feel reflects your mood that day.

Your calmness – Were you completely calm (a 10), completely anxious (a 0) or somewhere in between? Give it a 0-10 rating.

Your energy level – So lethargic you couldn't get out of bed (0) or totally energized all day long (10)? Or somewhere in between? – Give it a rating.

We keep track of mood, calmness and energy level because they are all variables that can affect your hair pulling, and they are also variables that are sensitive to most of the positive actions in the checklist. In other words, your positive actions can be expected to improve your mood, as well as make you calmer and more energetic, and also decrease your pulling.

Substances in the vice box – sugar, caffeine and alcohol – commonly affect mood, calmness and energy level, as well as pulling, in a negative way. So keeping track of these qualities will help you notice the effect these substances have on you personally. This is important. Gathering personal evidence that these food ingredients affect you will give you motivation to leave them out of your diet, much more so than just hearing or reading that they might be bad for you.

Pulling:

It's important to keep track of your hair pulling in some way. The easiest way is a 0-10 rating. You can decide whether you want 0 to represent zero pulling and 10 the worst you have ever done, or else you can do the opposite and stick with higher numbers being more positive, just like we did for mood, calmness or energy level.

If you prefer, you can keep track of your pulling in a different way. It can be helpful to keep track of the time spent pulling during the day, so you might want to keep track of minutes. Or you might find it more helpful to count the number of hairs you pull out, and record that instead. Choose what method you will use now, keeping in mind that you can always change it later.

There are a few reasons why we keep track of pulling. You can't make something better without putting some amount of attention on it, hence the saying "what gets measured gets managed."

Tracking your hair pulling is for the purpose of learning – it is how you learn the extent to which different interventions and positive actions included in the checklist affect your pulling. It is also how you learn how substances in the vice box affect your pulling, as well as how your mood, calmness and energy level are related to your pulling. You will learn what is true for you.

Another reason to track is that when you keep track of your pulling you cannot hide from it and pretend it doesn't exist. As much as you want to work on this problem now, there are going to be days when you really don't want to record in this book. Chances are, on those days you are also taking fewer, if any, positive actions, you are eating bad foods and you are doing more pulling. And you just don't feel like dealing with it.

Not recording in the Freedom Companion will let you off the hook. That is not good! It's letting yourself off the hook of the accountability that recording your actions provides, and you will backslide more for every day that you don't record. So, make a vow to yourself now that you will record in this book every day for 90 days straight. And if you slip for a day, don't feel like you've failed and might as well give up. Just get back to it the next day.

Before the end of 90 days, either make photocopies of one of the Daily Pages and put them in a binder or buy yourself another Freedom Companion so you can start all over again. You can make tremendous progress in 90 days, but in most cases you will need to stay on top of your pulling for more months or possibly years, depending how bad it is and how many changes and positive actions you are willing or able to do at once.

Don't forget that you may progress more quickly with a coach like me who can more specifically troubleshoot and direct you, or a therapist who can help you with deeper interpersonal issues that may be affecting your pulling.

Gratitude:

A hair pulling disorder typically includes a lot of focusing on "what's wrong." The hairs that feel different, coarser, out of place, and also simply the pulling itself and the negative consequences and feelings about it. A focus on something is energy that strengthens the thing you are focused on. Make sure you are focusing on something positive then! That is the purpose of this part of the positive log. Writing something you are grateful for, "counting your blessings," makes them count and gifts you with a more positively focused mind.

No matter how good or bad our circumstances are, our experience, including our happiness, depends on where we shine the spotlight of focus. A focus on what we have in life, the positives, makes us happier than does a focus on what we don't have, on the negatives of our life, which creates unhappiness.

When we are feeling positive emotions, we gravitate towards taking positive actions that we wouldn't be motivated to do if we were feeling negative.

Affirmation:

We get what we expect. Scientists are discovering that our brain chemistry is wired to produce the expected outcome. So when we write a statement expressing how we want to be, in the present tense, our brain starts to expect that and then it sets in motion biochemical changes that help us bring it about for real.

So for example, you can write "I am a calm and focused person." Or, "I have full and beautiful eyebrows." Or, "every day I am more and more in control of my life." By writing, reading and saying affirmations like these you will set in motion the thoughts, emotions and behaviors that work to bring about the brain's expectations.

Keep in mind that you may need to repeat affirmations many times for best effect. Just think how many opposite negative thoughts you have, or have had, and understand that writing or thinking or saying an affirmation once will not be nearly enough to counteract all of those negatives.

Positive Actions Checklist:

Recording your positive actions in a simple way, like a checklist, is satisfying. It's like giving yourself a gold star at the end of the day for a job well done. (Feel free to get some of those old foil stars (they still exist!) and reward yourself.)

It feels good to check things off and acknowledge yourself for your positive efforts, and scanning your positive actions checklist at the end of the day will help you to *remember* to take actions again the next day.

Ultimately, you hope to use some of the interventions every day so that they become positive habits that are working for you with very little decision-making effort and will-power needed.

I have included 26 specific positive actions in the checklist, starting with, "positive log," by which I mean you are writing in your Freedom Companion! (So you will have this one checked on every page.) I won't explain the rest of them here. Most are self-explanatory or can be found in articles about strategies to use for hair pulling, and the rest are either mentioned or discussed in detail in my book, "Skin Picking: The Freedom to Finally Stop." This Freedom Companion is meant to be a companion to that more comprehensive book, or any of the existing books on hair pulling.

The vice box (lower right). Here are three substances that commonly affect pulling in a negative way – sugar, caffeine and alcohol. It is well-worth reducing each of them to zero for a time to observe the effect they have on your pulling, as well as on your mood, calmness and energy level. (Read "Skin Picking: The Freedom to Finally Stop" for more on the topic, including how to do a trial sugar elimination.) Even if you don't reduce them to zero, keeping track of how much of each you have in a day will be instructive as you look over your day to see what you can learn.

I learned today: Here you can reflect and record something you learned about yourself and your pulling and about how any of the various positive or negative actions you took that day affected you. It can be something you learned while looking over the page at the end of the day, or it may be something you noticed earlier in the day. While you might not learn something new every single day, taking a moment to reflect can help you glean some new learning. And writing solidifies learning. You might have noticed something that flitted in your consciousness that day, but writing it down makes the learning more concrete. And looking back and reviewing your pages can help you learn more.

Pulling Log

The last couple of pages of the Freedom Companion consist of graph paper, on which you can graph your hair pulling as time passes. While there is no room to record the dates, every evening after recording your pulling in the Daily Pages, you can add a point on the graph the next square over from the day before. This way you will see your progress as the 90 days passes. You can also mark experiments you do as you go. For example, indicate all the days you do a sugar elimination so you can see the effect visually.

The Daily Pages

"The scariest moment is always just before you start."
- Stephen King

Date _____

Mood _____   Calmness _____   Energy Level _____   Pulling _____

Gratitude: _____

_____

Affirmation:

_____

_____

- [ ] Positive log (this page)
- [ ] 4-8-8 breathing
- [ ] Mindful check-ins
- [ ] Hat, scarf or ponytail
- [ ] Mascara or false eyelashes
- [ ] Bandages or fake nails
- [ ] Gloves
- [ ] Fidget toys
- [ ] Sensory tools
- [ ] Meditation or relaxation
- [ ] Enough sleep
- [ ] Good food
- [ ] Yoga

- [ ] Positive self-talk
- [ ] Questioned thoughts
- [ ] Reviewed thought flashcards
- [ ] Conditioner, cream, Vaseline
- [ ] Made schedule for tomorrow
- [ ] EFT tapping
- [ ] Hot bath +/- aromatherapy
- [ ] Mirror covered
- [ ] Time in nature
- [ ] Social engagement
- [ ] Drank water
- [ ] Supplements
- [ ] Exercise

I Learned Today:

Sugar	_____
Caffeine	_____
Alcohol	_____

_____

_____

_____

"And the day came when the risk to remain tight in a bud was more painful than the risk it took to blossom."
- Anais Nin

Date _____

Mood _____   Calmness _____   Energy Level _____   Pulling _____

Gratitude: _____
_____

Affirmation:
_____
_____

☐ Positive log (this page)
☐ 4-8-8 breathing
☐ Mindful check-ins
☐ Hat, scarf or ponytail
☐ Mascara or false eyelashes
☐ Bandages or fake nails
☐ Gloves
☐ Fidget toys
☐ Sensory tools
☐ Meditation or relaxation
☐ Enough sleep
☐ Good food
☐ Yoga

☐ Positive self-talk
☐ Questioned thoughts
☐ Reviewed thought flashcards
☐ Conditioner, cream, Vaseline
☐ Made schedule for tomorrow
☐ EFT tapping
☐ Hot bath +/- aromatherapy
☐ Mirror covered
☐ Time in nature
☐ Social engagement
☐ Drank water
☐ Supplements
☐ Exercise

I Learned Today:
_____
_____
_____

Sugar _____

Caffeine _____

Alcohol _____

"Nothing is particularly hard if you divide it into small jobs"
- Henry Ford

Date _____

Mood _____   Calmness _____   Energy Level _____   Pulling _____

Gratitude: _____

_____

Affirmation:

_____

_____

☐ Positive log (this page)   ☐ Positive self-talk
☐ 4-8-8 breathing   ☐ Questioned thoughts
☐ Mindful check-ins   ☐ Reviewed thought flashcards
☐ Hat, scarf or ponytail   ☐ Conditioner, cream, Vaseline
☐ Mascara or false eyelashes   ☐ Made schedule for tomorrow
☐ Bandages or fake nails   ☐ EFT tapping
☐ Gloves   ☐ Hot bath +/- aromatherapy
☐ Fidget toys   ☐ Mirror covered
☐ Sensory tools   ☐ Time in nature
☐ Meditation or relaxation   ☐ Social engagement
☐ Enough sleep   ☐ Drank water
☐ Good food   ☐ Supplements
☐ Yoga   ☐ Exercise

I Learned Today:

_____

_____

_____

Sugar _____

Caffeine _____

Alcohol _____

"An affirmation is a strong positive statement that something is already so."- Shakti Gawain

Date _____

Mood ____   Calmness ____   Energy Level ____   Pulling ____

Gratitude: _____
_____

Affirmation:
_____
_____

- [ ] Positive log (this page)
- [ ] 4-8-8 breathing
- [ ] Mindful check-ins
- [ ] Hat, scarf or ponytail
- [ ] Mascara or false eyelashes
- [ ] Bandages or fake nails
- [ ] Gloves
- [ ] Fidget toys
- [ ] Sensory tools
- [ ] Meditation or relaxation
- [ ] Enough sleep
- [ ] Good food
- [ ] Yoga

- [ ] Positive self-talk
- [ ] Questioned thoughts
- [ ] Reviewed thought flashcards
- [ ] Conditioner, cream, Vaseline
- [ ] Made schedule for tomorrow
- [ ] EFT tapping
- [ ] Hot bath +/- aromatherapy
- [ ] Mirror covered
- [ ] Time in nature
- [ ] Social engagement
- [ ] Drank water
- [ ] Supplements
- [ ] Exercise

I Learned Today:
_____
_____

Sugar _____

Caffeine _____

Alcohol _____

"Don't be afraid to fail. Be afraid not to try.
- Michael Jordan

Date _____

Mood _____   Calmness _____   Energy Level _____   Pulling _____

Gratitude: _____

_____

Affirmation:

_____

_____

☐ Positive log (this page)
☐ 4-8-8 breathing
☐ Mindful check-ins
☐ Hat, scarf or ponytail
☐ Mascara or false eyelashes
☐ Bandages or fake nails
☐ Gloves
☐ Fidget toys
☐ Sensory tools
☐ Meditation or relaxation
☐ Enough sleep
☐ Good food
☐ Yoga

☐ Positive self-talk
☐ Questioned thoughts
☐ Reviewed thought flashcards
☐ Conditioner, cream, Vaseline
☐ Made schedule for tomorrow
☐ EFT tapping
☐ Hot bath +/- aromatherapy
☐ Mirror covered
☐ Time in nature
☐ Social engagement
☐ Drank water
☐ Supplements
☐ Exercise

I Learned Today:

_____

_____

_____

Sugar _____

Caffeine _____

Alcohol _____

Date _____

Mood _____   Calmness _____   Energy Level _____   Pulling _____

Gratitude: _____

_____

Affirmation:

_____

_____

- ☐ Positive log (this page)
- ☐ 4-8-8 breathing
- ☐ Mindful check-ins
- ☐ Hat, scarf or ponytail
- ☐ Mascara or false eyelashes
- ☐ Bandages or fake nails
- ☐ Gloves
- ☐ Fidget toys
- ☐ Sensory tools
- ☐ Meditation or relaxation
- ☐ Enough sleep
- ☐ Good food
- ☐ Yoga

- ☐ Positive self-talk
- ☐ Questioned thoughts
- ☐ Reviewed thought flashcards
- ☐ Conditioner, cream, Vaseline
- ☐ Made schedule for tomorrow
- ☐ EFT tapping
- ☐ Hot bath +/- aromatherapy
- ☐ Mirror covered
- ☐ Time in nature
- ☐ Social engagement
- ☐ Drank water
- ☐ Supplements
- ☐ Exercise

I Learned Today:

_____

_____

_____

Sugar _____

Caffeine _____

Alcohol _____

"Love is the great miracle cure. Loving ourselves works miracles in our lives." - Louise L. Hay

Date _____

Mood _____   Calmness _____   Energy Level _____   Pulling _____

Gratitude: _____

_____

Affirmation:

_____

_____

- [ ] Positive log (this page)
- [ ] 4-8-8 breathing
- [ ] Mindful check-ins
- [ ] Hat, scarf or ponytail
- [ ] Mascara or false eyelashes
- [ ] Bandages or fake nails
- [ ] Gloves
- [ ] Fidget toys
- [ ] Sensory tools
- [ ] Meditation or relaxation
- [ ] Enough sleep
- [ ] Good food
- [ ] Yoga

- [ ] Positive self-talk
- [ ] Questioned thoughts
- [ ] Reviewed thought flashcards
- [ ] Conditioner, cream, Vaseline
- [ ] Made schedule for tomorrow
- [ ] EFT tapping
- [ ] Hot bath +/- aromatherapy
- [ ] Mirror covered
- [ ] Time in nature
- [ ] Social engagement
- [ ] Drank water
- [ ] Supplements
- [ ] Exercise

I Learned Today:

_____

_____

_____

Sugar _____

Caffeine _____

Alcohol _____

"Only in the darkness can you see the stars."
- Martin Luther King, Jr.

Date _____

Mood _____ Calmness _____ Energy Level _____ Pulling _____

Gratitude: _____

_____

Affirmation:

_____

_____

- [ ] Positive log (this page)
- [ ] 4-8-8 breathing
- [ ] Mindful check-ins
- [ ] Hat, scarf or ponytail
- [ ] Mascara or false eyelashes
- [ ] Bandages or fake nails
- [ ] Gloves
- [ ] Fidget toys
- [ ] Sensory tools
- [ ] Meditation or relaxation
- [ ] Enough sleep
- [ ] Good food
- [ ] Yoga

- [ ] Positive self-talk
- [ ] Questioned thoughts
- [ ] Reviewed thought flashcards
- [ ] Conditioner, cream, Vaseline
- [ ] Made schedule for tomorrow
- [ ] EFT tapping
- [ ] Hot bath +/- aromatherapy
- [ ] Mirror covered
- [ ] Time in nature
- [ ] Social engagement
- [ ] Drank water
- [ ] Supplements
- [ ] Exercise

I Learned Today:

_____

_____

_____

Sugar _____

Caffeine _____

Alcohol _____

"I find that the harder I work, the more luck I seem to have."
- Thomas Jefferson

Date _____

Mood _____   Calmness _____   Energy Level _____   Pulling _____

Gratitude: _____

_____

Affirmation:

_____

_____

- ☐ Positive log (this page)
- ☐ 4-8-8 breathing
- ☐ Mindful check-ins
- ☐ Hat, scarf or ponytail
- ☐ Mascara or false eyelashes
- ☐ Bandages or fake nails
- ☐ Gloves
- ☐ Fidget toys
- ☐ Sensory tools
- ☐ Meditation or relaxation
- ☐ Enough sleep
- ☐ Good food
- ☐ Yoga

- ☐ Positive self-talk
- ☐ Questioned thoughts
- ☐ Reviewed thought flashcards
- ☐ Conditioner, cream, Vaseline
- ☐ Made schedule for tomorrow
- ☐ EFT tapping
- ☐ Hot bath +/- aromatherapy
- ☐ Mirror covered
- ☐ Time in nature
- ☐ Social engagement
- ☐ Drank water
- ☐ Supplements
- ☐ Exercise

I Learned Today:

_____

_____

_____

Sugar _____

Caffeine _____

Alcohol _____

"Fall in love with the process, and the results will come."
- Eric Thomas

Date _____

Mood _____   Calmness _____   Energy Level _____   Pulling _____

Gratitude: _____

_____

Affirmation:

_____

_____

☐ Positive log (this page)	☐ Positive self-talk
☐ 4-8-8 breathing	☐ Questioned thoughts
☐ Mindful check-ins	☐ Reviewed thought flashcards
☐ Hat, scarf or ponytail	☐ Conditioner, cream, Vaseline
☐ Mascara or false eyelashes	☐ Made schedule for tomorrow
☐ Bandages or fake nails	☐ EFT tapping
☐ Gloves	☐ Hot bath +/- aromatherapy
☐ Fidget toys	☐ Mirror covered
☐ Sensory tools	☐ Time in nature
☐ Meditation or relaxation	☐ Social engagement
☐ Enough sleep	☐ Drank water
☐ Good food	☐ Supplements
☐ Yoga	☐ Exercise

I Learned Today:

_____

_____

_____

Sugar _____

Caffeine _____

Alcohol _____

"All you need to do to receive guidance is to ask for it and then listen."- Sanaya Roman

Date _____

Mood ____ Calmness ____ Energy Level ____ Pulling ____

Gratitude: _____

_____

Affirmation:

_____

_____

- ☐ Positive log (this page)
- ☐ 4-8-8 breathing
- ☐ Mindful check-ins
- ☐ Hat, scarf or ponytail
- ☐ Mascara or false eyelashes
- ☐ Bandages or fake nails
- ☐ Gloves
- ☐ Fidget toys
- ☐ Sensory tools
- ☐ Meditation or relaxation
- ☐ Enough sleep
- ☐ Good food
- ☐ Yoga

- ☐ Positive self-talk
- ☐ Questioned thoughts
- ☐ Reviewed thought flashcards
- ☐ Conditioner, cream, Vaseline
- ☐ Made schedule for tomorrow
- ☐ EFT tapping
- ☐ Hot bath +/- aromatherapy
- ☐ Mirror covered
- ☐ Time in nature
- ☐ Social engagement
- ☐ Drank water
- ☐ Supplements
- ☐ Exercise

I Learned Today:

_____

_____

_____

Sugar _____

Caffeine _____

Alcohol _____

"Smooth seas do not make skillful sailors."
- African proverb

Date _____

Mood _____ Calmness _____ Energy Level _____ Pulling _____

Gratitude: _____

_____

Affirmation:

_____

_____

☐ Positive log (this page)
☐ 4-8-8 breathing
☐ Mindful check-ins
☐ Hat, scarf or ponytail
☐ Mascara or false eyelashes
☐ Bandages or fake nails
☐ Gloves
☐ Fidget toys
☐ Sensory tools
☐ Meditation or relaxation
☐ Enough sleep
☐ Good food
☐ Yoga

☐ Positive self-talk
☐ Questioned thoughts
☐ Reviewed thought flashcards
☐ Conditioner, cream, Vaseline
☐ Made schedule for tomorrow
☐ EFT tapping
☐ Hot bath +/- aromatherapy
☐ Mirror covered
☐ Time in nature
☐ Social engagement
☐ Drank water
☐ Supplements
☐ Exercise

I Learned Today:

_____

_____

_____

Sugar _____

Caffeine _____

Alcohol _____

"A diamond is just a piece of charcoal that handled stress well"
– unknown

Mood _____ Calmness _____ Energy Level _____ Pulling _____

Gratitude: _____

_____

Affirmation:

_____

_____

- ☐ Positive log (this page)
- ☐ 4-8-8 breathing
- ☐ Mindful check-ins
- ☐ Hat, scarf or ponytail
- ☐ Mascara or false eyelashes
- ☐ Bandages or fake nails
- ☐ Gloves
- ☐ Fidget toys
- ☐ Sensory tools
- ☐ Meditation or relaxation
- ☐ Enough sleep
- ☐ Good food
- ☐ Yoga

- ☐ Positive self-talk
- ☐ Questioned thoughts
- ☐ Reviewed thought flashcards
- ☐ Conditioner, cream, Vaseline
- ☐ Made schedule for tomorrow
- ☐ EFT tapping
- ☐ Hot bath +/- aromatherapy
- ☐ Mirror covered
- ☐ Time in nature
- ☐ Social engagement
- ☐ Drank water
- ☐ Supplements
- ☐ Exercise

I Learned Today:

Sugar _____

Caffeine _____

Alcohol _____

_____

_____

_____

"To cease smoking is the easiest thing I ever did. I ought to know because I've done it a thousand times." – Mark Twain

Date _____

Mood _____ Calmness _____ Energy Level _____ Pulling _____

Gratitude: _____

_____

Affirmation:

_____

_____

- [ ] Positive log (this page)
- [ ] 4-8-8 breathing
- [ ] Mindful check-ins
- [ ] Hat, scarf or ponytail
- [ ] Mascara or false eyelashes
- [ ] Bandages or fake nails
- [ ] Gloves
- [ ] Fidget toys
- [ ] Sensory tools
- [ ] Meditation or relaxation
- [ ] Enough sleep
- [ ] Good food
- [ ] Yoga

- [ ] Positive self-talk
- [ ] Questioned thoughts
- [ ] Reviewed thought flashcards
- [ ] Conditioner, cream, Vaseline
- [ ] Made schedule for tomorrow
- [ ] EFT tapping
- [ ] Hot bath +/- aromatherapy
- [ ] Mirror covered
- [ ] Time in nature
- [ ] Social engagement
- [ ] Drank water
- [ ] Supplements
- [ ] Exercise

Sugar _____

Caffeine _____

Alcohol _____

I Learned Today:

_____

_____

_____

"We don't rise to the level of our expectations, we fall to the level of our training."- Archilochos   Date _____

Mood _____   Calmness _____   Energy Level _____   Pulling _____

Gratitude: _____

_____

Affirmation:

_____

_____

- ☐ Positive log (this page)
- ☐ 4-8-8 breathing
- ☐ Mindful check-ins
- ☐ Hat, scarf or ponytail
- ☐ Mascara or false eyelashes
- ☐ Bandages or fake nails
- ☐ Gloves
- ☐ Fidget toys
- ☐ Sensory tools
- ☐ Meditation or relaxation
- ☐ Enough sleep
- ☐ Good food
- ☐ Yoga

- ☐ Positive self-talk
- ☐ Questioned thoughts
- ☐ Reviewed thought flashcards
- ☐ Conditioner, cream, Vaseline
- ☐ Made schedule for tomorrow
- ☐ EFT tapping
- ☐ Hot bath +/- aromatherapy
- ☐ Mirror covered
- ☐ Time in nature
- ☐ Social engagement
- ☐ Drank water
- ☐ Supplements
- ☐ Exercise

I Learned Today:

_____

_____

_____

Sugar	_____
Caffeine	_____
Alcohol	_____

"Shoot for the moon. Even if you miss it you will land among the stars." - Les Brown

Date _____

Mood _____ Calmness _____ Energy Level _____ Pulling _____

Gratitude: _____

_____

Affirmation:

_____

_____

- [ ] Positive log (this page)
- [ ] 4-8-8 breathing
- [ ] Mindful check-ins
- [ ] Hat, scarf or ponytail
- [ ] Mascara or false eyelashes
- [ ] Bandages or fake nails
- [ ] Gloves
- [ ] Fidget toys
- [ ] Sensory tools
- [ ] Meditation or relaxation
- [ ] Enough sleep
- [ ] Good food
- [ ] Yoga

- [ ] Positive self-talk
- [ ] Questioned thoughts
- [ ] Reviewed thought flashcards
- [ ] Conditioner, cream, Vaseline
- [ ] Made schedule for tomorrow
- [ ] EFT tapping
- [ ] Hot bath +/- aromatherapy
- [ ] Mirror covered
- [ ] Time in nature
- [ ] Social engagement
- [ ] Drank water
- [ ] Supplements
- [ ] Exercise

I Learned Today:

_____

_____

_____

Sugar _____

Caffeine _____

Alcohol _____

"Many many tiny changes, over time, add up to transformation."
- Christina Pearson

Date _____

Mood ____   Calmness ____   Energy Level ____   Pulling ____

Gratitude: _____

_____

Affirmation:

_____

_____

☐ Positive log (this page)   ☐ Positive self-talk
☐ 4-8-8 breathing   ☐ Questioned thoughts
☐ Mindful check-ins   ☐ Reviewed thought flashcards
☐ Hat, scarf or ponytail   ☐ Conditioner, cream, Vaseline
☐ Mascara or false eyelashes   ☐ Made schedule for tomorrow
☐ Bandages or fake nails   ☐ EFT tapping
☐ Gloves   ☐ Hot bath +/- aromatherapy
☐ Fidget toys   ☐ Mirror covered
☐ Sensory tools   ☐ Time in nature
☐ Meditation or relaxation   ☐ Social engagement
☐ Enough sleep   ☐ Drank water
☐ Good food   ☐ Supplements
☐ Yoga   ☐ Exercise

I Learned Today:

_____

Sugar	_____
Caffeine	_____
Alcohol	_____

_____

_____

"A lifetime can well be spent correcting and improving one's own faults without bothering about others."
- Edward Weston

Date _____

Mood ____   Calmness _____   Energy Level _____   Pulling ____

Gratitude: _____

_____

Affirmation:

_____

_____

☐ Positive log (this page)   ☐ Positive self-talk
☐ 4-8-8 breathing   ☐ Questioned thoughts
☐ Mindful check-ins   ☐ Reviewed thought flashcards
☐ Hat, scarf or ponytail   ☐ Conditioner, cream, Vaseline
☐ Mascara or false eyelashes   ☐ Made schedule for tomorrow
☐ Bandages or fake nails   ☐ EFT tapping
☐ Gloves   ☐ Hot bath +/- aromatherapy
☐ Fidget toys   ☐ Mirror covered
☐ Sensory tools   ☐ Time in nature
☐ Meditation or relaxation   ☐ Social engagement
☐ Enough sleep   ☐ Drank water
☐ Good food   ☐ Supplements
☐ Yoga   ☐ Exercise

I Learned Today:

_____

_____

_____

Sugar _____

Caffeine _____

Alcohol _____

"The time to relax is when you don't have time for it."
- Sydney J. Harris

Date _____

Mood _____   Calmness _____   Energy Level _____   Pulling _____

Gratitude: _____
_____

Affirmation:
_____
_____

- [ ] Positive log (this page)
- [ ] 4-8-8 breathing
- [ ] Mindful check-ins
- [ ] Hat, scarf or ponytail
- [ ] Mascara or false eyelashes
- [ ] Bandages or fake nails
- [ ] Gloves
- [ ] Fidget toys
- [ ] Sensory tools
- [ ] Meditation or relaxation
- [ ] Enough sleep
- [ ] Good food
- [ ] Yoga

- [ ] Positive self-talk
- [ ] Questioned thoughts
- [ ] Reviewed thought flashcards
- [ ] Conditioner, cream, Vaseline
- [ ] Made schedule for tomorrow
- [ ] EFT tapping
- [ ] Hot bath +/- aromatherapy
- [ ] Mirror covered
- [ ] Time in nature
- [ ] Social engagement
- [ ] Drank water
- [ ] Supplements
- [ ] Exercise

I Learned Today:
_____
_____
_____

Sugar _____

Caffeine _____

Alcohol _____

"The best time to plant a tree was 20 years ago. The second best time is now." - Chinese Proverb

Date _____

Mood _____ Calmness _____ Energy Level _____ Pulling _____

Gratitude: _____

_____

Affirmation:

_____

_____

- ☐ Positive log (this page)
- ☐ 4-8-8 breathing
- ☐ Mindful check-ins
- ☐ Hat, scarf or ponytail
- ☐ Mascara or false eyelashes
- ☐ Bandages or fake nails
- ☐ Gloves
- ☐ Fidget toys
- ☐ Sensory tools
- ☐ Meditation or relaxation
- ☐ Enough sleep
- ☐ Good food
- ☐ Yoga

- ☐ Positive self-talk
- ☐ Questioned thoughts
- ☐ Reviewed thought flashcards
- ☐ Conditioner, cream, Vaseline
- ☐ Made schedule for tomorrow
- ☐ EFT tapping
- ☐ Hot bath +/- aromatherapy
- ☐ Mirror covered
- ☐ Time in nature
- ☐ Social engagement
- ☐ Drank water
- ☐ Supplements
- ☐ Exercise

I Learned Today:

_____

_____

_____

Sugar _____

Caffeine _____

Alcohol _____

"Believe you can and you're halfway there."
—Theodore Roosevelt

Mood _____   Calmness _____   Energy Level _____   Pulling _____

Gratitude: _____

_____

Affirmation:

_____

_____

- ☐ Positive log (this page)
- ☐ 4-8-8 breathing
- ☐ Mindful check-ins
- ☐ Hat, scarf or ponytail
- ☐ Mascara or false eyelashes
- ☐ Bandages or fake nails
- ☐ Gloves
- ☐ Fidget toys
- ☐ Sensory tools
- ☐ Meditation or relaxation
- ☐ Enough sleep
- ☐ Good food
- ☐ Yoga

- ☐ Positive self-talk
- ☐ Questioned thoughts
- ☐ Reviewed thought flashcards
- ☐ Conditioner, cream, Vaseline
- ☐ Made schedule for tomorrow
- ☐ EFT tapping
- ☐ Hot bath +/- aromatherapy
- ☐ Mirror covered
- ☐ Time in nature
- ☐ Social engagement
- ☐ Drank water
- ☐ Supplements
- ☐ Exercise

I Learned Today:

_____

_____

_____

Sugar _____

Caffeine _____

Alcohol _____

Date _____

Mood _____   Calmness _____   Energy Level _____   Pulling _____

Gratitude: _____

_____

Affirmation:

_____

_____

- [ ] Positive log (this page)
- [ ] 4-8-8 breathing
- [ ] Mindful check-ins
- [ ] Hat, scarf or ponytail
- [ ] Mascara or false eyelashes
- [ ] Bandages or fake nails
- [ ] Gloves
- [ ] Fidget toys
- [ ] Sensory tools
- [ ] Meditation or relaxation
- [ ] Enough sleep
- [ ] Good food
- [ ] Yoga

- [ ] Positive self-talk
- [ ] Questioned thoughts
- [ ] Reviewed thought flashcards
- [ ] Conditioner, cream, Vaseline
- [ ] Made schedule for tomorrow
- [ ] EFT tapping
- [ ] Hot bath +/- aromatherapy
- [ ] Mirror covered
- [ ] Time in nature
- [ ] Social engagement
- [ ] Drank water
- [ ] Supplements
- [ ] Exercise

I Learned Today:

_____

_____

_____

Sugar _____

Caffeine _____

Alcohol _____

"When everything seems to be going against you, remember that the airplane takes off against the wind, not with it."
- Henry Ford

Date _____

Mood _____   Calmness _____   Energy Level _____   Pulling _____

Gratitude: _____

_____

Affirmation:

_____

_____

☐ Positive log (this page)
☐ 4-8-8 breathing
☐ Mindful check-ins
☐ Hat, scarf or ponytail
☐ Mascara or false eyelashes
☐ Bandages or fake nails
☐ Gloves
☐ Fidget toys
☐ Sensory tools
☐ Meditation or relaxation
☐ Enough sleep
☐ Good food
☐ Yoga

☐ Positive self-talk
☐ Questioned thoughts
☐ Reviewed thought flashcards
☐ Conditioner, cream, Vaseline
☐ Made schedule for tomorrow
☐ EFT tapping
☐ Hot bath +/- aromatherapy
☐ Mirror covered
☐ Time in nature
☐ Social engagement
☐ Drank water
☐ Supplements
☐ Exercise

I Learned Today:

_____

_____

_____

Sugar _____

Caffeine _____

Alcohol _____

"Rule your mind or it will rule you."
- Horace

Date _____

Mood _____   Calmness _____   Energy Level _____   Pulling _____

Gratitude: _____

_____

Affirmation:

_____

_____

☐ Positive log (this page)	☐ Positive self-talk
☐ 4-8-8 breathing	☐ Questioned thoughts
☐ Mindful check-ins	☐ Reviewed thought flashcards
☐ Hat, scarf or ponytail	☐ Conditioner, cream, Vaseline
☐ Mascara or false eyelashes	☐ Made schedule for tomorrow
☐ Bandages or fake nails	☐ EFT tapping
☐ Gloves	☐ Hot bath +/- aromatherapy
☐ Fidget toys	☐ Mirror covered
☐ Sensory tools	☐ Time in nature
☐ Meditation or relaxation	☐ Social engagement
☐ Enough sleep	☐ Drank water
☐ Good food	☐ Supplements
☐ Yoga	☐ Exercise

I Learned Today:

_____

_____

_____

Sugar _____

Caffeine _____

Alcohol _____

"A goal without a plan is just a wish."
- Antoine de Saint-Exupery

Date _____

Mood _____   Calmness _____   Energy Level _____   Pulling _____

Gratitude: _____

_____

Affirmation:

_____

_____

- [ ] Positive log (this page)
- [ ] 4-8-8 breathing
- [ ] Mindful check-ins
- [ ] Hat, scarf or ponytail
- [ ] Mascara or false eyelashes
- [ ] Bandages or fake nails
- [ ] Gloves
- [ ] Fidget toys
- [ ] Sensory tools
- [ ] Meditation or relaxation
- [ ] Enough sleep
- [ ] Good food
- [ ] Yoga

- [ ] Positive self-talk
- [ ] Questioned thoughts
- [ ] Reviewed thought flashcards
- [ ] Conditioner, cream, Vaseline
- [ ] Made schedule for tomorrow
- [ ] EFT tapping
- [ ] Hot bath +/- aromatherapy
- [ ] Mirror covered
- [ ] Time in nature
- [ ] Social engagement
- [ ] Drank water
- [ ] Supplements
- [ ] Exercise

I Learned Today:

_____

_____

_____

Sugar _____

Caffeine _____

Alcohol _____

"Words are a form of action, capable of influencing change."
- Ingrid Bengis

Date _____

Mood _____ Calmness _____ Energy Level _____ Pulling _____

Gratitude: _____

_____

Affirmation:

_____

_____

☐ Positive log (this page)   ☐ Positive self-talk
☐ 4-8-8 breathing   ☐ Questioned thoughts
☐ Mindful check-ins   ☐ Reviewed thought flashcards
☐ Hat, scarf or ponytail   ☐ Conditioner, cream, Vaseline
☐ Mascara or false eyelashes   ☐ Made schedule for tomorrow
☐ Bandages or fake nails   ☐ EFT tapping
☐ Gloves   ☐ Hot bath +/- aromatherapy
☐ Fidget toys   ☐ Mirror covered
☐ Sensory tools   ☐ Time in nature
☐ Meditation or relaxation   ☐ Social engagement
☐ Enough sleep   ☐ Drank water
☐ Good food   ☐ Supplements
☐ Yoga   ☐ Exercise

I Learned Today:

_____

_____

_____

Sugar _____

Caffeine _____

Alcohol _____

"The secret of your future is hidden in your daily routine."
- Mike Murdock

Date _____

Mood _____   Calmness _____   Energy Level _____   Pulling _____

Gratitude: _____

_____

Affirmation:

_____

_____

- [ ] Positive log (this page)
- [ ] 4-8-8 breathing
- [ ] Mindful check-ins
- [ ] Hat, scarf or ponytail
- [ ] Mascara or false eyelashes
- [ ] Bandages or fake nails
- [ ] Gloves
- [ ] Fidget toys
- [ ] Sensory tools
- [ ] Meditation or relaxation
- [ ] Enough sleep
- [ ] Good food
- [ ] Yoga

- [ ] Positive self-talk
- [ ] Questioned thoughts
- [ ] Reviewed thought flashcards
- [ ] Conditioner, cream, Vaseline
- [ ] Made schedule for tomorrow
- [ ] EFT tapping
- [ ] Hot bath +/- aromatherapy
- [ ] Mirror covered
- [ ] Time in nature
- [ ] Social engagement
- [ ] Drank water
- [ ] Supplements
- [ ] Exercise

I Learned Today:

_____

_____

_____

Sugar	_____
Caffeine	_____
Alcohol	_____

Date _____

Mood ____   Calmness ____   Energy Level ____   Pulling ____

Gratitude: _____

_____

Affirmation:

_____

_____

- ☐ Positive log (this page)
- ☐ 4-8-8 breathing
- ☐ Mindful check-ins
- ☐ Hat, scarf or ponytail
- ☐ Mascara or false eyelashes
- ☐ Bandages or fake nails
- ☐ Gloves
- ☐ Fidget toys
- ☐ Sensory tools
- ☐ Meditation or relaxation
- ☐ Enough sleep
- ☐ Good food
- ☐ Yoga

- ☐ Positive self-talk
- ☐ Questioned thoughts
- ☐ Reviewed thought flashcards
- ☐ Conditioner, cream, Vaseline
- ☐ Made schedule for tomorrow
- ☐ EFT tapping
- ☐ Hot bath +/- aromatherapy
- ☐ Mirror covered
- ☐ Time in nature
- ☐ Social engagement
- ☐ Drank water
- ☐ Supplements
- ☐ Exercise

I Learned Today:

_____

_____

_____

Sugar _____

Caffeine _____

Alcohol _____

"The only remedy for bad habits is counter habits."
- Swami Vivekananda

Date _____

Mood _____ Calmness _____ Energy Level _____ Pulling _____

Gratitude: _____

_____

Affirmation:

_____

_____

☐ Positive log (this page)   ☐ Positive self-talk
☐ 4-8-8 breathing   ☐ Questioned thoughts
☐ Mindful check-ins   ☐ Reviewed thought flashcards
☐ Hat, scarf or ponytail   ☐ Conditioner, cream, Vaseline
☐ Mascara or false eyelashes ☐ Made schedule for tomorrow
☐ Bandages or fake nails   ☐ EFT tapping
☐ Gloves   ☐ Hot bath +/- aromatherapy
☐ Fidget toys   ☐ Mirror covered
☐ Sensory tools   ☐ Time in nature
☐ Meditation or relaxation   ☐ Social engagement
☐ Enough sleep   ☐ Drank water
☐ Good food   ☐ Supplements
☐ Yoga   ☐ Exercise

I Learned Today:

_____

_____

_____

Sugar _____

Caffeine _____

Alcohol _____

"Hold on to what is good, even if it's a handful of earth."
-- Hopi prayer

Date _____

Mood ____   Calmness ____   Energy Level ____   Pulling ____

Gratitude: _____

_____

Affirmation:

_____

_____

☐ Positive log (this page)   ☐ Positive self-talk
☐ 4-8-8 breathing   ☐ Questioned thoughts
☐ Mindful check-ins   ☐ Reviewed thought flashcards
☐ Hat, scarf or ponytail   ☐ Conditioner, cream, Vaseline
☐ Mascara or false eyelashes   ☐ Made schedule for tomorrow
☐ Bandages or fake nails   ☐ EFT tapping
☐ Gloves   ☐ Hot bath +/- aromatherapy
☐ Fidget toys   ☐ Mirror covered
☐ Sensory tools   ☐ Time in nature
☐ Meditation or relaxation   ☐ Social engagement
☐ Enough sleep   ☐ Drank water
☐ Good food   ☐ Supplements
☐ Yoga   ☐ Exercise

I Learned Today:

_____

_____

_____

Sugar _____

Caffeine _____

Alcohol _____

"If you don't like how things are, change it! You're not a tree."
- Jim Rohn

Date _____

Mood _____   Calmness _____   Energy Level _____   Pulling _____

Gratitude: _____

_____

Affirmation:

_____

_____

- ☐ Positive log (this page)
- ☐ 4-8-8 breathing
- ☐ Mindful check-ins
- ☐ Hat, scarf or ponytail
- ☐ Mascara or false eyelashes
- ☐ Bandages or fake nails
- ☐ Gloves
- ☐ Fidget toys
- ☐ Sensory tools
- ☐ Meditation or relaxation
- ☐ Enough sleep
- ☐ Good food
- ☐ Yoga

- ☐ Positive self-talk
- ☐ Questioned thoughts
- ☐ Reviewed thought flashcards
- ☐ Conditioner, cream, Vaseline
- ☐ Made schedule for tomorrow
- ☐ EFT tapping
- ☐ Hot bath +/- aromatherapy
- ☐ Mirror covered
- ☐ Time in nature
- ☐ Social engagement
- ☐ Drank water
- ☐ Supplements
- ☐ Exercise

I Learned Today:

_____

_____

_____

Sugar _____

Caffeine _____

Alcohol _____

"I have not failed. I've just found 10,000 ways that won't work."
- Thomas Edison

Date _____

Mood ____   Calmness ____   Energy Level ____   Pulling ____

Gratitude: _____

_____

Affirmation:

_____

_____

- [ ] Positive log (this page)
- [ ] 4-8-8 breathing
- [ ] Mindful check-ins
- [ ] Hat, scarf or ponytail
- [ ] Mascara or false eyelashes
- [ ] Bandages or fake nails
- [ ] Gloves
- [ ] Fidget toys
- [ ] Sensory tools
- [ ] Meditation or relaxation
- [ ] Enough sleep
- [ ] Good food
- [ ] Yoga

- [ ] Positive self-talk
- [ ] Questioned thoughts
- [ ] Reviewed thought flashcards
- [ ] Conditioner, cream, Vaseline
- [ ] Made schedule for tomorrow
- [ ] EFT tapping
- [ ] Hot bath +/- aromatherapy
- [ ] Mirror covered
- [ ] Time in nature
- [ ] Social engagement
- [ ] Drank water
- [ ] Supplements
- [ ] Exercise

I Learned Today:

_____

_____

_____

Sugar _____

Caffeine _____

Alcohol _____

"Dreaming, after all, is a form of planning."
- Gloria Steinem

Mood _____   Calmness _____   Energy Level _____   Pulling _____

Gratitude: _____

_____

Affirmation:

_____

_____

☐ Positive log (this page)   ☐ Positive self-talk
☐ 4-8-8 breathing   ☐ Questioned thoughts
☐ Mindful check-ins   ☐ Reviewed thought flashcards
☐ Hat, scarf or ponytail   ☐ Conditioner, cream, Vaseline
☐ Mascara or false eyelashes   ☐ Made schedule for tomorrow
☐ Bandages or fake nails   ☐ EFT tapping
☐ Gloves   ☐ Hot bath +/- aromatherapy
☐ Fidget toys   ☐ Mirror covered
☐ Sensory tools   ☐ Time in nature
☐ Meditation or relaxation   ☐ Social engagement
☐ Enough sleep   ☐ Drank water
☐ Good food   ☐ Supplements
☐ Yoga   ☐ Exercise

I Learned Today:

Sugar _____

Caffeine _____

Alcohol _____

_____
_____
_____

"To ease another's heartache is to forget one's own."
- Abraham Lincoln

Mood _____   Calmness _____   Energy Level _____   Pulling _____

Gratitude: _____

_____

Affirmation:

_____

_____

☐ Positive log (this page)   ☐ Positive self-talk
☐ 4-8-8 breathing   ☐ Questioned thoughts
☐ Mindful check-ins   ☐ Reviewed thought flashcards
☐ Hat, scarf or ponytail   ☐ Conditioner, cream, Vaseline
☐ Mascara or false eyelashes   ☐ Made schedule for tomorrow
☐ Bandages or fake nails   ☐ EFT tapping
☐ Gloves   ☐ Hot bath +/- aromatherapy
☐ Fidget toys   ☐ Mirror covered
☐ Sensory tools   ☐ Time in nature
☐ Meditation or relaxation   ☐ Social engagement
☐ Enough sleep   ☐ Drank water
☐ Good food   ☐ Supplements
☐ Yoga   ☐ Exercise

I Learned Today:

_____

_____

_____

Sugar _____

Caffeine _____

Alcohol _____

"A year from now, you may wish you had started today."
- Karen Lamb

Date _____

Mood _____   Calmness _____   Energy Level _____   Pulling _____

Gratitude: _____

_____

Affirmation:

_____

_____

- [ ] Positive log (this page)
- [ ] 4-8-8 breathing
- [ ] Mindful check-ins
- [ ] Hat, scarf or ponytail
- [ ] Mascara or false eyelashes
- [ ] Bandages or fake nails
- [ ] Gloves
- [ ] Fidget toys
- [ ] Sensory tools
- [ ] Meditation or relaxation
- [ ] Enough sleep
- [ ] Good food
- [ ] Yoga

- [ ] Positive self-talk
- [ ] Questioned thoughts
- [ ] Reviewed thought flashcards
- [ ] Conditioner, cream, Vaseline
- [ ] Made schedule for tomorrow
- [ ] EFT tapping
- [ ] Hot bath +/- aromatherapy
- [ ] Mirror covered
- [ ] Time in nature
- [ ] Social engagement
- [ ] Drank water
- [ ] Supplements
- [ ] Exercise

I Learned Today:

_____

_____

_____

Sugar _____

Caffeine _____

Alcohol _____

"If you don't want to slip, don't go where it's slippery."
- Alcoholics Anonymous

Mood _____   Calmness _____   Energy Level _____   Pulling _____

Gratitude: _____

_____

Affirmation:

_____

_____

☐ Positive log (this page)	☐ Positive self-talk
☐ 4-8-8 breathing	☐ Questioned thoughts
☐ Mindful check-ins	☐ Reviewed thought flashcards
☐ Hat, scarf or ponytail	☐ Conditioner, cream, Vaseline
☐ Mascara or false eyelashes	☐ Made schedule for tomorrow
☐ Bandages or fake nails	☐ EFT tapping
☐ Gloves	☐ Hot bath +/- aromatherapy
☐ Fidget toys	☐ Mirror covered
☐ Sensory tools	☐ Time in nature
☐ Meditation or relaxation	☐ Social engagement
☐ Enough sleep	☐ Drank water
☐ Good food	☐ Supplements
☐ Yoga	☐ Exercise

I Learned Today:

_____

_____

_____

Sugar	_____
Caffeine	_____
Alcohol	_____

"Nothing is impossible, the word itself says I'm possible."
- Audrey Hepburn

Date _____

Mood _____   Calmness _____   Energy Level _____   Pulling _____

Gratitude: _____

_____

Affirmation:

_____

_____

☐ Positive log (this page)   ☐ Positive self-talk
☐ 4-8-8 breathing   ☐ Questioned thoughts
☐ Mindful check-ins   ☐ Reviewed thought flashcards
☐ Hat, scarf or ponytail   ☐ Conditioner, cream, Vaseline
☐ Mascara or false eyelashes   ☐ Made schedule for tomorrow
☐ Bandages or fake nails   ☐ EFT tapping
☐ Gloves   ☐ Hot bath +/- aromatherapy
☐ Fidget toys   ☐ Mirror covered
☐ Sensory tools   ☐ Time in nature
☐ Meditation or relaxation   ☐ Social engagement
☐ Enough sleep   ☐ Drank water
☐ Good food   ☐ Supplements
☐ Yoga   ☐ Exercise

I Learned Today:

_____

_____

_____

Sugar _____

Caffeine _____

Alcohol _____

Date _____

Mood _____   Calmness _____   Energy Level _____   Pulling _____

Gratitude: _____

_____

Affirmation:

_____

_____

- [ ] Positive log (this page)
- [ ] 4-8-8 breathing
- [ ] Mindful check-ins
- [ ] Hat, scarf or ponytail
- [ ] Mascara or false eyelashes
- [ ] Bandages or fake nails
- [ ] Gloves
- [ ] Fidget toys
- [ ] Sensory tools
- [ ] Meditation or relaxation
- [ ] Enough sleep
- [ ] Good food
- [ ] Yoga

- [ ] Positive self-talk
- [ ] Questioned thoughts
- [ ] Reviewed thought flashcards
- [ ] Conditioner, cream, Vaseline
- [ ] Made schedule for tomorrow
- [ ] EFT tapping
- [ ] Hot bath +/- aromatherapy
- [ ] Mirror covered
- [ ] Time in nature
- [ ] Social engagement
- [ ] Drank water
- [ ] Supplements
- [ ] Exercise

I Learned Today:

_____

_____

_____

Sugar	_____
Caffeine	_____
Alcohol	_____

"Concentrate all your thoughts upon the work in hand. The Sun's rays do not burn until brought to a focus."
- Alexander Graham Bell

Date _____

Mood ____   Calmness ____   Energy Level ____   Pulling ____

Gratitude: _____
_____

Affirmation:
_____

_____

- [ ] Positive log (this page)
- [ ] 4-8-8 breathing
- [ ] Mindful check-ins
- [ ] Hat, scarf or ponytail
- [ ] Mascara or false eyelashes
- [ ] Bandages or fake nails
- [ ] Gloves
- [ ] Fidget toys
- [ ] Sensory tools
- [ ] Meditation or relaxation
- [ ] Enough sleep
- [ ] Good food
- [ ] Yoga

- [ ] Positive self-talk
- [ ] Questioned thoughts
- [ ] Reviewed thought flashcards
- [ ] Conditioner, cream, Vaseline
- [ ] Made schedule for tomorrow
- [ ] EFT tapping
- [ ] Hot bath +/- aromatherapy
- [ ] Mirror covered
- [ ] Time in nature
- [ ] Social engagement
- [ ] Drank water
- [ ] Supplements
- [ ] Exercise

I Learned Today:
_____

_____

_____

Sugar _____

Caffeine _____

Alcohol _____

"You miss 100% of the shots you don't take."
—Wayne Gretzky

Date _____

Mood _____ Calmness _____ Energy Level _____ Pulling _____

Gratitude: _____

_____

Affirmation:

_____

_____

- ☐ Positive log (this page)
- ☐ 4-8-8 breathing
- ☐ Mindful check-ins
- ☐ Hat, scarf or ponytail
- ☐ Mascara or false eyelashes
- ☐ Bandages or fake nails
- ☐ Gloves
- ☐ Fidget toys
- ☐ Sensory tools
- ☐ Meditation or relaxation
- ☐ Enough sleep
- ☐ Good food
- ☐ Yoga

- ☐ Positive self-talk
- ☐ Questioned thoughts
- ☐ Reviewed thought flashcards
- ☐ Conditioner, cream, Vaseline
- ☐ Made schedule for tomorrow
- ☐ EFT tapping
- ☐ Hot bath +/- aromatherapy
- ☐ Mirror covered
- ☐ Time in nature
- ☐ Social engagement
- ☐ Drank water
- ☐ Supplements
- ☐ Exercise

I Learned Today:

_____

_____

_____

Sugar _____

Caffeine _____

Alcohol _____

"The way I see it, if you want the rainbow, you gotta put up with the rain." - Dolly Parton

Date _____

Mood _____ Calmness _____ Energy Level _____ Pulling _____

Gratitude: _____

_____

Affirmation:

_____

_____

- ☐ Positive log (this page)
- ☐ 4-8-8 breathing
- ☐ Mindful check-ins
- ☐ Hat, scarf or ponytail
- ☐ Mascara or false eyelashes
- ☐ Bandages or fake nails
- ☐ Gloves
- ☐ Fidget toys
- ☐ Sensory tools
- ☐ Meditation or relaxation
- ☐ Enough sleep
- ☐ Good food
- ☐ Yoga

- ☐ Positive self-talk
- ☐ Questioned thoughts
- ☐ Reviewed thought flashcards
- ☐ Conditioner, cream, Vaseline
- ☐ Made schedule for tomorrow
- ☐ EFT tapping
- ☐ Hot bath +/- aromatherapy
- ☐ Mirror covered
- ☐ Time in nature
- ☐ Social engagement
- ☐ Drank water
- ☐ Supplements
- ☐ Exercise

I Learned Today:

_____

_____

_____

Sugar	_____
Caffeine	_____
Alcohol	_____

"The person who says it cannot be done should not interrupt the person who is doing it." – Chinese Proverb

Date _____

Mood _____ Calmness _____ Energy Level _____ Pulling _____

Gratitude: _____

_____

Affirmation:

_____

_____

☐ Positive log (this page)
☐ 4-8-8 breathing
☐ Mindful check-ins
☐ Hat, scarf or ponytail
☐ Mascara or false eyelashes
☐ Bandages or fake nails
☐ Gloves
☐ Fidget toys
☐ Sensory tools
☐ Meditation or relaxation
☐ Enough sleep
☐ Good food
☐ Yoga

☐ Positive self-talk
☐ Questioned thoughts
☐ Reviewed thought flashcards
☐ Conditioner, cream, Vaseline
☐ Made schedule for tomorrow
☐ EFT tapping
☐ Hot bath +/- aromatherapy
☐ Mirror covered
☐ Time in nature
☐ Social engagement
☐ Drank water
☐ Supplements
☐ Exercise

I Learned Today:

_____

_____

_____

Sugar _____

Caffeine _____

Alcohol _____

"I attribute my success to this: I never gave or took any excuse."
– Florence Nightingale

Date _____

Mood ____   Calmness ____   Energy Level ____   Pulling ____

Gratitude: _____

_____

Affirmation:

_____

_____

- ☐ Positive log (this page)
- ☐ 4-8-8 breathing
- ☐ Mindful check-ins
- ☐ Hat, scarf or ponytail
- ☐ Mascara or false eyelashes
- ☐ Bandages or fake nails
- ☐ Gloves
- ☐ Fidget toys
- ☐ Sensory tools
- ☐ Meditation or relaxation
- ☐ Enough sleep
- ☐ Good food
- ☐ Yoga

- ☐ Positive self-talk
- ☐ Questioned thoughts
- ☐ Reviewed thought flashcards
- ☐ Conditioner, cream, Vaseline
- ☐ Made schedule for tomorrow
- ☐ EFT tapping
- ☐ Hot bath +/- aromatherapy
- ☐ Mirror covered
- ☐ Time in nature
- ☐ Social engagement
- ☐ Drank water
- ☐ Supplements
- ☐ Exercise

I Learned Today:

_____

_____

_____

Sugar _____

Caffeine _____

Alcohol _____

Date _____

Mood _____   Calmness _____   Energy Level _____   Pulling _____

Gratitude: _____

_____

Affirmation:

_____

_____

- [ ] Positive log (this page)
- [ ] 4-8-8 breathing
- [ ] Mindful check-ins
- [ ] Hat, scarf or ponytail
- [ ] Mascara or false eyelashes
- [ ] Bandages or fake nails
- [ ] Gloves
- [ ] Fidget toys
- [ ] Sensory tools
- [ ] Meditation or relaxation
- [ ] Enough sleep
- [ ] Good food
- [ ] Yoga

- [ ] Positive self-talk
- [ ] Questioned thoughts
- [ ] Reviewed thought flashcards
- [ ] Conditioner, cream, Vaseline
- [ ] Made schedule for tomorrow
- [ ] EFT tapping
- [ ] Hot bath +/- aromatherapy
- [ ] Mirror covered
- [ ] Time in nature
- [ ] Social engagement
- [ ] Drank water
- [ ] Supplements
- [ ] Exercise

I Learned Today:

_____

_____

_____

Sugar _____

Caffeine _____

Alcohol _____

"Our sorrows and wounds are healed only when we touch them with compassion."
- Buddha

Date _____

Mood _____   Calmness _____   Energy Level _____   Pulling _____

Gratitude: _____

_____

Affirmation:

_____

_____

☐ Positive log (this page)   ☐ Positive self-talk
☐ 4-8-8 breathing   ☐ Questioned thoughts
☐ Mindful check-ins   ☐ Reviewed thought flashcards
☐ Hat, scarf or ponytail   ☐ Conditioner, cream, Vaseline
☐ Mascara or false eyelashes   ☐ Made schedule for tomorrow
☐ Bandages or fake nails   ☐ EFT tapping
☐ Gloves   ☐ Hot bath +/- aromatherapy
☐ Fidget toys   ☐ Mirror covered
☐ Sensory tools   ☐ Time in nature
☐ Meditation or relaxation   ☐ Social engagement
☐ Enough sleep   ☐ Drank water
☐ Good food   ☐ Supplements
☐ Yoga   ☐ Exercise

I Learned Today:

_____

_____

_____

Sugar _____

Caffeine _____

Alcohol _____

'Beauty is how you feel inside, and it reflects in your eyes. It is not something physical.'
- Sophia Loren

Date _____

Mood _____   Calmness _____   Energy Level _____   Pulling _____

Gratitude: _____

_____

Affirmation:

_____

_____

☐ Positive log (this page)	☐ Positive self-talk
☐ 4-8-8 breathing	☐ Questioned thoughts
☐ Mindful check-ins	☐ Reviewed thought flashcards
☐ Hat, scarf or ponytail	☐ Conditioner, cream, Vaseline
☐ Mascara or false eyelashes	☐ Made schedule for tomorrow
☐ Bandages or fake nails	☐ EFT tapping
☐ Gloves	☐ Hot bath +/- aromatherapy
☐ Fidget toys	☐ Mirror covered
☐ Sensory tools	☐ Time in nature
☐ Meditation or relaxation	☐ Social engagement
☐ Enough sleep	☐ Drank water
☐ Good food	☐ Supplements
☐ Yoga	☐ Exercise

I Learned Today:

_____

_____

_____

Sugar _____

Caffeine _____

Alcohol _____

"If you're going through hell, keep going!"
- Winston Churchill

Date _____

Mood _____   Calmness _____   Energy Level _____   Pulling _____

Gratitude: _____

_____

Affirmation:

_____

_____

- ☐ Positive log (this page)
- ☐ 4-8-8 breathing
- ☐ Mindful check-ins
- ☐ Hat, scarf or ponytail
- ☐ Mascara or false eyelashes
- ☐ Bandages or fake nails
- ☐ Gloves
- ☐ Fidget toys
- ☐ Sensory tools
- ☐ Meditation or relaxation
- ☐ Enough sleep
- ☐ Good food
- ☐ Yoga

- ☐ Positive self-talk
- ☐ Questioned thoughts
- ☐ Reviewed thought flashcards
- ☐ Conditioner, cream, Vaseline
- ☐ Made schedule for tomorrow
- ☐ EFT tapping
- ☐ Hot bath +/- aromatherapy
- ☐ Mirror covered
- ☐ Time in nature
- ☐ Social engagement
- ☐ Drank water
- ☐ Supplements
- ☐ Exercise

Sugar _____

Caffeine _____

Alcohol _____

I Learned Today:

_____

_____

_____

"Nothing will work unless you do."
- Maya Angelou

Date _____

Mood ____ Calmness ____ Energy Level ____ Pulling ____

Gratitude: _____

_____

Affirmation:

_____

_____

- [ ] Positive log (this page)
- [ ] 4-8-8 breathing
- [ ] Mindful check-ins
- [ ] Hat, scarf or ponytail
- [ ] Mascara or false eyelashes
- [ ] Bandages or fake nails
- [ ] Gloves
- [ ] Fidget toys
- [ ] Sensory tools
- [ ] Meditation or relaxation
- [ ] Enough sleep
- [ ] Good food
- [ ] Yoga

- [ ] Positive self-talk
- [ ] Questioned thoughts
- [ ] Reviewed thought flashcards
- [ ] Conditioner, cream, Vaseline
- [ ] Made schedule for tomorrow
- [ ] EFT tapping
- [ ] Hot bath +/- aromatherapy
- [ ] Mirror covered
- [ ] Time in nature
- [ ] Social engagement
- [ ] Drank water
- [ ] Supplements
- [ ] Exercise

I Learned Today:

_____

_____

_____

Sugar _____

Caffeine _____

Alcohol _____

"Surround yourself with people who respect and treat you well."
- Claudia Black

Date _____

Mood _____ Calmness _____ Energy Level _____ Pulling _____

Gratitude: _____

_____

Affirmation:

_____

_____

- [ ] Positive log (this page)
- [ ] 4-8-8 breathing
- [ ] Mindful check-ins
- [ ] Hat, scarf or ponytail
- [ ] Mascara or false eyelashes
- [ ] Bandages or fake nails
- [ ] Gloves
- [ ] Fidget toys
- [ ] Sensory tools
- [ ] Meditation or relaxation
- [ ] Enough sleep
- [ ] Good food
- [ ] Yoga

- [ ] Positive self-talk
- [ ] Questioned thoughts
- [ ] Reviewed thought flashcards
- [ ] Conditioner, cream, Vaseline
- [ ] Made schedule for tomorrow
- [ ] EFT tapping
- [ ] Hot bath +/- aromatherapy
- [ ] Mirror covered
- [ ] Time in nature
- [ ] Social engagement
- [ ] Drank water
- [ ] Supplements
- [ ] Exercise

I Learned Today:

_____

_____

_____

Sugar _____

Caffeine _____

Alcohol _____

Date _____

Mood _____   Calmness _____   Energy Level _____   Pulling _____

Gratitude: _____

_____

Affirmation:

_____

_____

- [ ] Positive log (this page)
- [ ] 4-8-8 breathing
- [ ] Mindful check-ins
- [ ] Hat, scarf or ponytail
- [ ] Mascara or false eyelashes
- [ ] Bandages or fake nails
- [ ] Gloves
- [ ] Fidget toys
- [ ] Sensory tools
- [ ] Meditation or relaxation
- [ ] Enough sleep
- [ ] Good food
- [ ] Yoga

- [ ] Positive self-talk
- [ ] Questioned thoughts
- [ ] Reviewed thought flashcards
- [ ] Conditioner, cream, Vaseline
- [ ] Made schedule for tomorrow
- [ ] EFT tapping
- [ ] Hot bath +/- aromatherapy
- [ ] Mirror covered
- [ ] Time in nature
- [ ] Social engagement
- [ ] Drank water
- [ ] Supplements
- [ ] Exercise

I Learned Today:

_____

_____

_____

Sugar _____

Caffeine _____

Alcohol _____

"It's kind of fun to do the impossible."
- Walt Disney

Date _____

Mood _____   Calmness _____   Energy Level _____   Pulling _____

Gratitude: _____

_____

Affirmation:

_____

_____

- ☐ Positive log (this page)
- ☐ 4-8-8 breathing
- ☐ Mindful check-ins
- ☐ Hat, scarf or ponytail
- ☐ Mascara or false eyelashes
- ☐ Bandages or fake nails
- ☐ Gloves
- ☐ Fidget toys
- ☐ Sensory tools
- ☐ Meditation or relaxation
- ☐ Enough sleep
- ☐ Good food
- ☐ Yoga

- ☐ Positive self-talk
- ☐ Questioned thoughts
- ☐ Reviewed thought flashcards
- ☐ Conditioner, cream, Vaseline
- ☐ Made schedule for tomorrow
- ☐ EFT tapping
- ☐ Hot bath +/- aromatherapy
- ☐ Mirror covered
- ☐ Time in nature
- ☐ Social engagement
- ☐ Drank water
- ☐ Supplements
- ☐ Exercise

Sugar _____

Caffeine _____

Alcohol _____

I Learned Today:

_____

_____

_____

"Ever tried. Ever failed. No matter. Try again. Fail again. Fail better." - Samuel Beckett

Date _____

Mood _____ Calmness _____ Energy Level _____ Pulling _____

Gratitude: _____

_____

Affirmation:

_____

_____

☐ Positive log (this page)
☐ 4-8-8 breathing
☐ Mindful check-ins
☐ Hat, scarf or ponytail
☐ Mascara or false eyelashes
☐ Bandages or fake nails
☐ Gloves
☐ Fidget toys
☐ Sensory tools
☐ Meditation or relaxation
☐ Enough sleep
☐ Good food
☐ Yoga

☐ Positive self-talk
☐ Questioned thoughts
☐ Reviewed thought flashcards
☐ Conditioner, cream, Vaseline
☐ Made schedule for tomorrow
☐ EFT tapping
☐ Hot bath +/- aromatherapy
☐ Mirror covered
☐ Time in nature
☐ Social engagement
☐ Drank water
☐ Supplements
☐ Exercise

I Learned Today:

_____

_____

_____

Sugar _____

Caffeine _____

Alcohol _____

"We have been taught to believe that negative equals realistic and positive equals unrealistic." - Susan Jeffers

Date _____

Mood _____   Calmness _____   Energy Level _____   Pulling _____

Gratitude: _____

_____

Affirmation:

_____

_____

- ☐ Positive log (this page)
- ☐ 4-8-8 breathing
- ☐ Mindful check-ins
- ☐ Hat, scarf or ponytail
- ☐ Mascara or false eyelashes
- ☐ Bandages or fake nails
- ☐ Gloves
- ☐ Fidget toys
- ☐ Sensory tools
- ☐ Meditation or relaxation
- ☐ Enough sleep
- ☐ Good food
- ☐ Yoga

- ☐ Positive self-talk
- ☐ Questioned thoughts
- ☐ Reviewed thought flashcards
- ☐ Conditioner, cream, Vaseline
- ☐ Made schedule for tomorrow
- ☐ EFT tapping
- ☐ Hot bath +/- aromatherapy
- ☐ Mirror covered
- ☐ Time in nature
- ☐ Social engagement
- ☐ Drank water
- ☐ Supplements
- ☐ Exercise

I Learned Today:

_____

_____

_____

Sugar _____

Caffeine _____

Alcohol _____

"Everyday do something that will inch you closer to a better tomorrow." - Doug Firebaugh

Date _____

Mood _____   Calmness _____   Energy Level _____   Pulling _____

Gratitude: _____

_____

Affirmation:

_____

_____

- [ ] Positive log (this page)
- [ ] 4-8-8 breathing
- [ ] Mindful check-ins
- [ ] Hat, scarf or ponytail
- [ ] Mascara or false eyelashes
- [ ] Bandages or fake nails
- [ ] Gloves
- [ ] Fidget toys
- [ ] Sensory tools
- [ ] Meditation or relaxation
- [ ] Enough sleep
- [ ] Good food
- [ ] Yoga

- [ ] Positive self-talk
- [ ] Questioned thoughts
- [ ] Reviewed thought flashcards
- [ ] Conditioner, cream, Vaseline
- [ ] Made schedule for tomorrow
- [ ] EFT tapping
- [ ] Hot bath +/- aromatherapy
- [ ] Mirror covered
- [ ] Time in nature
- [ ] Social engagement
- [ ] Drank water
- [ ] Supplements
- [ ] Exercise

I Learned Today:

_____

_____

_____

Sugar _____

Caffeine _____

Alcohol _____

"Anxiety is a warning from the unconscious mind to focus on what you want" – Tad James

Date _____

Mood _____   Calmness _____   Energy Level _____   Pulling _____

Gratitude: _____

_____

Affirmation:

_____

_____

- [ ] Positive log (this page)
- [ ] 4-8-8 breathing
- [ ] Mindful check-ins
- [ ] Hat, scarf or ponytail
- [ ] Mascara or false eyelashes
- [ ] Bandages or fake nails
- [ ] Gloves
- [ ] Fidget toys
- [ ] Sensory tools
- [ ] Meditation or relaxation
- [ ] Enough sleep
- [ ] Good food
- [ ] Yoga

- [ ] Positive self-talk
- [ ] Questioned thoughts
- [ ] Reviewed thought flashcards
- [ ] Conditioner, cream, Vaseline
- [ ] Made schedule for tomorrow
- [ ] EFT tapping
- [ ] Hot bath +/- aromatherapy
- [ ] Mirror covered
- [ ] Time in nature
- [ ] Social engagement
- [ ] Drank water
- [ ] Supplements
- [ ] Exercise

I Learned Today:

_____

_____

_____

Sugar _____

Caffeine _____

Alcohol _____

"Sometimes your joy is the source of your smile, but sometimes your smile can be the source of your joy."
Thich Nhat Hanh

Date _____

Mood _____   Calmness _____   Energy Level _____   Pulling _____

Gratitude: _____

_____

Affirmation:

_____

_____

- ☐ Positive log (this page)
- ☐ 4-8-8 breathing
- ☐ Mindful check-ins
- ☐ Hat, scarf or ponytail
- ☐ Mascara or false eyelashes
- ☐ Bandages or fake nails
- ☐ Gloves
- ☐ Fidget toys
- ☐ Sensory tools
- ☐ Meditation or relaxation
- ☐ Enough sleep
- ☐ Good food
- ☐ Yoga

- ☐ Positive self-talk
- ☐ Questioned thoughts
- ☐ Reviewed thought flashcards
- ☐ Conditioner, cream, Vaseline
- ☐ Made schedule for tomorrow
- ☐ EFT tapping
- ☐ Hot bath +/- aromatherapy
- ☐ Mirror covered
- ☐ Time in nature
- ☐ Social engagement
- ☐ Drank water
- ☐ Supplements
- ☐ Exercise

I Learned Today:

_____

_____

_____

Sugar _____

Caffeine _____

Alcohol _____

"Life shrinks or expands in proportion to one's courage."
–Anais Nin

Date _____

Mood _____ Calmness _____ Energy Level _____ Pulling _____

Gratitude: _____

_____

Affirmation:

_____

_____

☐ Positive log (this page)   ☐ Positive self-talk
☐ 4-8-8 breathing   ☐ Questioned thoughts
☐ Mindful check-ins   ☐ Reviewed thought flashcards
☐ Hat, scarf or ponytail   ☐ Conditioner, cream, Vaseline
☐ Mascara or false eyelashes   ☐ Made schedule for tomorrow
☐ Bandages or fake nails   ☐ EFT tapping
☐ Gloves   ☐ Hot bath +/- aromatherapy
☐ Fidget toys   ☐ Mirror covered
☐ Sensory tools   ☐ Time in nature
☐ Meditation or relaxation   ☐ Social engagement
☐ Enough sleep   ☐ Drank water
☐ Good food   ☐ Supplements
☐ Yoga   ☐ Exercise

I Learned Today:

_____

_____

_____

Sugar _____

Caffeine _____

Alcohol _____

"You become what you believe."
– Oprah Winfrey

Date _____

Mood _____   Calmness _____   Energy Level _____   Pulling _____

Gratitude: _____

_____

Affirmation:

_____

_____

- [ ] Positive log (this page)
- [ ] 4-8-8 breathing
- [ ] Mindful check-ins
- [ ] Hat, scarf or ponytail
- [ ] Mascara or false eyelashes
- [ ] Bandages or fake nails
- [ ] Gloves
- [ ] Fidget toys
- [ ] Sensory tools
- [ ] Meditation or relaxation
- [ ] Enough sleep
- [ ] Good food
- [ ] Yoga

- [ ] Positive self-talk
- [ ] Questioned thoughts
- [ ] Reviewed thought flashcards
- [ ] Conditioner, cream, Vaseline
- [ ] Made schedule for tomorrow
- [ ] EFT tapping
- [ ] Hot bath +/- aromatherapy
- [ ] Mirror covered
- [ ] Time in nature
- [ ] Social engagement
- [ ] Drank water
- [ ] Supplements
- [ ] Exercise

I Learned Today:

_____

_____

_____

Sugar	_____
Caffeine	_____
Alcohol	_____

Date _____

Mood ____   Calmness ____   Energy Level ____   Pulling ____

Gratitude: _____

_____

Affirmation:

_____

_____

- ☐ Positive log (this page)
- ☐ 4-8-8 breathing
- ☐ Mindful check-ins
- ☐ Hat, scarf or ponytail
- ☐ Mascara or false eyelashes
- ☐ Bandages or fake nails
- ☐ Gloves
- ☐ Fidget toys
- ☐ Sensory tools
- ☐ Meditation or relaxation
- ☐ Enough sleep
- ☐ Good food
- ☐ Yoga

- ☐ Positive self-talk
- ☐ Questioned thoughts
- ☐ Reviewed thought flashcards
- ☐ Conditioner, cream, Vaseline
- ☐ Made schedule for tomorrow
- ☐ EFT tapping
- ☐ Hot bath +/- aromatherapy
- ☐ Mirror covered
- ☐ Time in nature
- ☐ Social engagement
- ☐ Drank water
- ☐ Supplements
- ☐ Exercise

I Learned Today:

_____

_____

_____

Sugar _____

Caffeine _____

Alcohol _____

"People always ask me how long it takes to do my hair. I don't know, I'm never there."
- Dolly Parton

Date _____

Mood _____ Calmness _____ Energy Level _____ Pulling _____

Gratitude: _____

_____

Affirmation:

_____

_____

- ☐ Positive log (this page)
- ☐ 4-8-8 breathing
- ☐ Mindful check-ins
- ☐ Hat, scarf or ponytail
- ☐ Mascara or false eyelashes
- ☐ Bandages or fake nails
- ☐ Gloves
- ☐ Fidget toys
- ☐ Sensory tools
- ☐ Meditation or relaxation
- ☐ Enough sleep
- ☐ Good food
- ☐ Yoga

- ☐ Positive self-talk
- ☐ Questioned thoughts
- ☐ Reviewed thought flashcards
- ☐ Conditioner, cream, Vaseline
- ☐ Made schedule for tomorrow
- ☐ EFT tapping
- ☐ Hot bath +/- aromatherapy
- ☐ Mirror covered
- ☐ Time in nature
- ☐ Social engagement
- ☐ Drank water
- ☐ Supplements
- ☐ Exercise

I Learned Today:

_____

_____

_____

Sugar _____

Caffeine _____

Alcohol _____

"Remember, be gentle."
- Christina Pearson

Date _____

Mood _____   Calmness _____   Energy Level _____   Pulling _____

Gratitude: _____

_____

Affirmation:

_____

_____

☐ Positive log (this page)   ☐ Positive self-talk
☐ 4-8-8 breathing   ☐ Questioned thoughts
☐ Mindful check-ins   ☐ Reviewed thought flashcards
☐ Hat, scarf or ponytail   ☐ Conditioner, cream, Vaseline
☐ Mascara or false eyelashes   ☐ Made schedule for tomorrow
☐ Bandages or fake nails   ☐ EFT tapping
☐ Gloves   ☐ Hot bath +/- aromatherapy
☐ Fidget toys   ☐ Mirror covered
☐ Sensory tools   ☐ Time in nature
☐ Meditation or relaxation   ☐ Social engagement
☐ Enough sleep   ☐ Drank water
☐ Good food   ☐ Supplements
☐ Yoga   ☐ Exercise

I Learned Today:

Sugar _____

Caffeine _____

Alcohol _____

_____
_____
_____

Date _____

Mood _____   Calmness _____   Energy Level _____   Pulling _____

Gratitude: _____

_____

Affirmation:

_____

_____

- [ ] Positive log (this page)
- [ ] 4-8-8 breathing
- [ ] Mindful check-ins
- [ ] Hat, scarf or ponytail
- [ ] Mascara or false eyelashes
- [ ] Bandages or fake nails
- [ ] Gloves
- [ ] Fidget toys
- [ ] Sensory tools
- [ ] Meditation or relaxation
- [ ] Enough sleep
- [ ] Good food
- [ ] Yoga

- [ ] Positive self-talk
- [ ] Questioned thoughts
- [ ] Reviewed thought flashcards
- [ ] Conditioner, cream, Vaseline
- [ ] Made schedule for tomorrow
- [ ] EFT tapping
- [ ] Hot bath +/- aromatherapy
- [ ] Mirror covered
- [ ] Time in nature
- [ ] Social engagement
- [ ] Drank water
- [ ] Supplements
- [ ] Exercise

I Learned Today:

_____

_____

_____

Sugar _____

Caffeine _____

Alcohol _____

"Learn to get in touch with the silence within yourself and know that everything in this life has a purpose."
- Elisabeth Kubler-Ross

Date _____

Mood ____   Calmness ____   Energy Level ____   Pulling ____

Gratitude: _____

_____

Affirmation:

_____

_____

- [ ] Positive log (this page)
- [ ] 4-8-8 breathing
- [ ] Mindful check-ins
- [ ] Hat, scarf or ponytail
- [ ] Mascara or false eyelashes
- [ ] Bandages or fake nails
- [ ] Gloves
- [ ] Fidget toys
- [ ] Sensory tools
- [ ] Meditation or relaxation
- [ ] Enough sleep
- [ ] Good food
- [ ] Yoga

- [ ] Positive self-talk
- [ ] Questioned thoughts
- [ ] Reviewed thought flashcards
- [ ] Conditioner, cream, Vaseline
- [ ] Made schedule for tomorrow
- [ ] EFT tapping
- [ ] Hot bath +/- aromatherapy
- [ ] Mirror covered
- [ ] Time in nature
- [ ] Social engagement
- [ ] Drank water
- [ ] Supplements
- [ ] Exercise

I Learned Today:

_____

_____

_____

Sugar _____

Caffeine _____

Alcohol _____

"Being happy doesn't mean that everything is perfect. It means that you've decided to look beyond the imperfections."
- Gerard Way

Date _____

Mood _____   Calmness _____   Energy Level _____   Pulling _____

Gratitude: _____

_____

Affirmation:

_____

_____

☐ Positive log (this page)   ☐ Positive self-talk
☐ 4-8-8 breathing   ☐ Questioned thoughts
☐ Mindful check-ins   ☐ Reviewed thought flashcards
☐ Hat, scarf or ponytail   ☐ Conditioner, cream, Vaseline
☐ Mascara or false eyelashes   ☐ Made schedule for tomorrow
☐ Bandages or fake nails   ☐ EFT tapping
☐ Gloves   ☐ Hot bath +/- aromatherapy
☐ Fidget toys   ☐ Mirror covered
☐ Sensory tools   ☐ Time in nature
☐ Meditation or relaxation   ☐ Social engagement
☐ Enough sleep   ☐ Drank water
☐ Good food   ☐ Supplements
☐ Yoga   ☐ Exercise

I Learned Today:

_____

_____

_____

Sugar _____

Caffeine _____

Alcohol _____

"Remember no one can make you feel inferior without your consent."
- Eleanor Roosevelt

Date _____

Mood _____   Calmness _____   Energy Level _____   Pulling _____

Gratitude: _____

_____

Affirmation:

_____

_____

☐ Positive log (this page)
☐ 4-8-8 breathing
☐ Mindful check-ins
☐ Hat, scarf or ponytail
☐ Mascara or false eyelashes
☐ Bandages or fake nails
☐ Gloves
☐ Fidget toys
☐ Sensory tools
☐ Meditation or relaxation
☐ Enough sleep
☐ Good food
☐ Yoga

☐ Positive self-talk
☐ Questioned thoughts
☐ Reviewed thought flashcards
☐ Conditioner, cream, Vaseline
☐ Made schedule for tomorrow
☐ EFT tapping
☐ Hot bath +/- aromatherapy
☐ Mirror covered
☐ Time in nature
☐ Social engagement
☐ Drank water
☐ Supplements
☐ Exercise

I Learned Today:

_____

_____

_____

Sugar _____

Caffeine _____

Alcohol _____

"Never give up, for that is just the place and time that the tide will turn."
- Harriet Beecher Stowe

Date _____

Mood _____   Calmness _____   Energy Level _____   Pulling _____

Gratitude: _____

_____

Affirmation:

_____

_____

☐ Positive log (this page)	☐ Positive self-talk
☐ 4-8-8 breathing	☐ Questioned thoughts
☐ Mindful check-ins	☐ Reviewed thought flashcards
☐ Hat, scarf or ponytail	☐ Conditioner, cream, Vaseline
☐ Mascara or false eyelashes	☐ Made schedule for tomorrow
☐ Bandages or fake nails	☐ EFT tapping
☐ Gloves	☐ Hot bath +/- aromatherapy
☐ Fidget toys	☐ Mirror covered
☐ Sensory tools	☐ Time in nature
☐ Meditation or relaxation	☐ Social engagement
☐ Enough sleep	☐ Drank water
☐ Good food	☐ Supplements
☐ Yoga	☐ Exercise

I Learned Today:

_____

_____

_____

Sugar _____

Caffeine _____

Alcohol _____

"Saying no can be the ultimate self-care."
- Claudia Black

Date _____

Mood _____   Calmness _____   Energy Level _____   Pulling _____

Gratitude: _____

_____

Affirmation:

_____

_____

☐ Positive log (this page)   ☐ Positive self-talk
☐ 4-8-8 breathing   ☐ Questioned thoughts
☐ Mindful check-ins   ☐ Reviewed thought flashcards
☐ Hat, scarf or ponytail   ☐ Conditioner, cream, Vaseline
☐ Mascara or false eyelashes   ☐ Made schedule for tomorrow
☐ Bandages or fake nails   ☐ EFT tapping
☐ Gloves   ☐ Hot bath +/- aromatherapy
☐ Fidget toys   ☐ Mirror covered
☐ Sensory tools   ☐ Time in nature
☐ Meditation or relaxation   ☐ Social engagement
☐ Enough sleep   ☐ Drank water
☐ Good food   ☐ Supplements
☐ Yoga   ☐ Exercise

I Learned Today:

_____

_____

_____

Sugar _____

Caffeine _____

Alcohol _____

"People say that motivation doesn't last. Well, neither does bathing. That's why we recommend it daily."
- Zig Ziglar

Date _____

Mood _____   Calmness _____   Energy Level _____   Pulling _____

Gratitude: _____

_____

Affirmation:

_____

_____

- [ ] Positive log (this page)
- [ ] 4-8-8 breathing
- [ ] Mindful check-ins
- [ ] Hat, scarf or ponytail
- [ ] Mascara or false eyelashes
- [ ] Bandages or fake nails
- [ ] Gloves
- [ ] Fidget toys
- [ ] Sensory tools
- [ ] Meditation or relaxation
- [ ] Enough sleep
- [ ] Good food
- [ ] Yoga

- [ ] Positive self-talk
- [ ] Questioned thoughts
- [ ] Reviewed thought flashcards
- [ ] Conditioner, cream, Vaseline
- [ ] Made schedule for tomorrow
- [ ] EFT tapping
- [ ] Hot bath +/- aromatherapy
- [ ] Mirror covered
- [ ] Time in nature
- [ ] Social engagement
- [ ] Drank water
- [ ] Supplements
- [ ] Exercise

I Learned Today:

_____

_____

_____

Sugar _____

Caffeine _____

Alcohol _____

"If you hear a voice within you say "you cannot paint," then by all means paint and that voice will be silenced."
—Vincent Van Gogh

Date _____

Mood _____   Calmness _____   Energy Level _____   Pulling _____

Gratitude: _____

_____

Affirmation:

_____

_____

☐ Positive log (this page)   ☐ Positive self-talk
☐ 4-8-8 breathing   ☐ Questioned thoughts
☐ Mindful check-ins   ☐ Reviewed thought flashcards
☐ Hat, scarf or ponytail   ☐ Conditioner, cream, Vaseline
☐ Mascara or false eyelashes   ☐ Made schedule for tomorrow
☐ Bandages or fake nails   ☐ EFT tapping
☐ Gloves   ☐ Hot bath +/- aromatherapy
☐ Fidget toys   ☐ Mirror covered
☐ Sensory tools   ☐ Time in nature
☐ Meditation or relaxation   ☐ Social engagement
☐ Enough sleep   ☐ Drank water
☐ Good food   ☐ Supplements
☐ Yoga   ☐ Exercise

I Learned Today:

_____

_____

_____

Sugar _____

Caffeine _____

Alcohol _____

Date _____

Mood _____   Calmness _____   Energy Level _____   Pulling _____

Gratitude: _____

_____

Affirmation:

_____

_____

- ☐ Positive log (this page)
- ☐ 4-8-8 breathing
- ☐ Mindful check-ins
- ☐ Hat, scarf or ponytail
- ☐ Mascara or false eyelashes
- ☐ Bandages or fake nails
- ☐ Gloves
- ☐ Fidget toys
- ☐ Sensory tools
- ☐ Meditation or relaxation
- ☐ Enough sleep
- ☐ Good food
- ☐ Yoga

- ☐ Positive self-talk
- ☐ Questioned thoughts
- ☐ Reviewed thought flashcards
- ☐ Conditioner, cream, Vaseline
- ☐ Made schedule for tomorrow
- ☐ EFT tapping
- ☐ Hot bath +/- aromatherapy
- ☐ Mirror covered
- ☐ Time in nature
- ☐ Social engagement
- ☐ Drank water
- ☐ Supplements
- ☐ Exercise

I Learned Today:

_____

_____

_____

Sugar _____

Caffeine _____

Alcohol _____

"If you do what you've always done, you'll get what you've always gotten." – Tony Robbins   Date _____

Mood _____   Calmness _____   Energy Level _____   Pulling _____

Gratitude: _____

_____

Affirmation:

_____

_____

- [ ] Positive log (this page)
- [ ] 4-8-8 breathing
- [ ] Mindful check-ins
- [ ] Hat, scarf or ponytail
- [ ] Mascara or false eyelashes
- [ ] Bandages or fake nails
- [ ] Gloves
- [ ] Fidget toys
- [ ] Sensory tools
- [ ] Meditation or relaxation
- [ ] Enough sleep
- [ ] Good food
- [ ] Yoga

- [ ] Positive self-talk
- [ ] Questioned thoughts
- [ ] Reviewed thought flashcards
- [ ] Conditioner, cream, Vaseline
- [ ] Made schedule for tomorrow
- [ ] EFT tapping
- [ ] Hot bath +/- aromatherapy
- [ ] Mirror covered
- [ ] Time in nature
- [ ] Social engagement
- [ ] Drank water
- [ ] Supplements
- [ ] Exercise

I Learned Today:

_____

_____

_____

Sugar _____

Caffeine _____

Alcohol _____

"Eighty percent of success is showing up."
– Woody Allen

Date _____

Mood _____   Calmness _____   Energy Level _____   Pulling _____

Gratitude: _____

_____

Affirmation:

_____

_____

☐ Positive log (this page)   ☐ Positive self-talk
☐ 4-8-8 breathing   ☐ Questioned thoughts
☐ Mindful check-ins   ☐ Reviewed thought flashcards
☐ Hat, scarf or ponytail   ☐ Conditioner, cream, Vaseline
☐ Mascara or false eyelashes   ☐ Made schedule for tomorrow
☐ Bandages or fake nails   ☐ EFT tapping
☐ Gloves   ☐ Hot bath +/- aromatherapy
☐ Fidget toys   ☐ Mirror covered
☐ Sensory tools   ☐ Time in nature
☐ Meditation or relaxation   ☐ Social engagement
☐ Enough sleep   ☐ Drank water
☐ Good food   ☐ Supplements
☐ Yoga   ☐ Exercise

I Learned Today:

_____

_____

_____

Sugar	_____
Caffeine	_____
Alcohol	_____

"So much has been given to me, I have not time to ponder over that which has been denied."
- Helen Keller

Date _____

Mood _____   Calmness _____   Energy Level _____   Pulling _____

Gratitude: _____

_____

Affirmation:

_____

_____

☐ Positive log (this page)	☐ Positive self-talk
☐ 4-8-8 breathing	☐ Questioned thoughts
☐ Mindful check-ins	☐ Reviewed thought flashcards
☐ Hat, scarf or ponytail	☐ Conditioner, cream, Vaseline
☐ Mascara or false eyelashes	☐ Made schedule for tomorrow
☐ Bandages or fake nails	☐ EFT tapping
☐ Gloves	☐ Hot bath +/- aromatherapy
☐ Fidget toys	☐ Mirror covered
☐ Sensory tools	☐ Time in nature
☐ Meditation or relaxation	☐ Social engagement
☐ Enough sleep	☐ Drank water
☐ Good food	☐ Supplements
☐ Yoga	☐ Exercise

I Learned Today:

_____

Sugar _____

_____

Caffeine _____

_____

Alcohol _____

"The season of failure is the best time for sowing the seeds of success."
- Yogananda Paramahamsa

Date _____

Mood ____   Calmness ____   Energy Level ____   Pulling ____

Gratitude: _____

_____

Affirmation:

_____

_____

- ☐ Positive log (this page)
- ☐ 4-8-8 breathing
- ☐ Mindful check-ins
- ☐ Hat, scarf or ponytail
- ☐ Mascara or false eyelashes
- ☐ Bandages or fake nails
- ☐ Gloves
- ☐ Fidget toys
- ☐ Sensory tools
- ☐ Meditation or relaxation
- ☐ Enough sleep
- ☐ Good food
- ☐ Yoga

- ☐ Positive self-talk
- ☐ Questioned thoughts
- ☐ Reviewed thought flashcards
- ☐ Conditioner, cream, Vaseline
- ☐ Made schedule for tomorrow
- ☐ EFT tapping
- ☐ Hot bath +/- aromatherapy
- ☐ Mirror covered
- ☐ Time in nature
- ☐ Social engagement
- ☐ Drank water
- ☐ Supplements
- ☐ Exercise

I Learned Today:

_____

_____

_____

Sugar _____

Caffeine _____

Alcohol _____

"One does not discover new lands without consenting to lose sight of the shore for a very long time."
- Andre Gide

Date _____

Mood _____   Calmness _____   Energy Level _____   Pulling _____

Gratitude: _____

_____

Affirmation:

_____

_____

- [ ] Positive log (this page)
- [ ] 4-8-8 breathing
- [ ] Mindful check-ins
- [ ] Hat, scarf or ponytail
- [ ] Mascara or false eyelashes
- [ ] Bandages or fake nails
- [ ] Gloves
- [ ] Fidget toys
- [ ] Sensory tools
- [ ] Meditation or relaxation
- [ ] Enough sleep
- [ ] Good food
- [ ] Yoga

- [ ] Positive self-talk
- [ ] Questioned thoughts
- [ ] Reviewed thought flashcards
- [ ] Conditioner, cream, Vaseline
- [ ] Made schedule for tomorrow
- [ ] EFT tapping
- [ ] Hot bath +/- aromatherapy
- [ ] Mirror covered
- [ ] Time in nature
- [ ] Social engagement
- [ ] Drank water
- [ ] Supplements
- [ ] Exercise

I Learned Today:

_____

_____

_____

Sugar _____

Caffeine _____

Alcohol _____

Date _____

Mood _____   Calmness _____   Energy Level _____   Pulling _____

Gratitude: _____
_____

Affirmation:
_____
_____

- [ ] Positive log (this page)
- [ ] 4-8-8 breathing
- [ ] Mindful check-ins
- [ ] Hat, scarf or ponytail
- [ ] Mascara or false eyelashes
- [ ] Bandages or fake nails
- [ ] Gloves
- [ ] Fidget toys
- [ ] Sensory tools
- [ ] Meditation or relaxation
- [ ] Enough sleep
- [ ] Good food
- [ ] Yoga

- [ ] Positive self-talk
- [ ] Questioned thoughts
- [ ] Reviewed thought flashcards
- [ ] Conditioner, cream, Vaseline
- [ ] Made schedule for tomorrow
- [ ] EFT tapping
- [ ] Hot bath +/- aromatherapy
- [ ] Mirror covered
- [ ] Time in nature
- [ ] Social engagement
- [ ] Drank water
- [ ] Supplements
- [ ] Exercise

I Learned Today:
_____
_____
_____

Sugar _____

Caffeine _____

Alcohol _____

"If you can't fly then run, if you can't run then walk, if you can't walk then crawl, but whatever you do you have to keep moving forward."
- Martin Luther King Jr.

Date _____

Mood _____   Calmness _____   Energy Level _____   Pulling _____

Gratitude:

_____

_____

Affirmation:

_____

_____

☐ Positive log (this page)
☐ 4-8-8 breathing
☐ Mindful check-ins
☐ Hat, scarf or ponytail
☐ Mascara or false eyelashes
☐ Bandages or fake nails
☐ Gloves
☐ Fidget toys
☐ Sensory tools
☐ Meditation or relaxation
☐ Enough sleep
☐ Good food
☐ Yoga

☐ Positive self-talk
☐ Questioned thoughts
☐ Reviewed thought flashcards
☐ Conditioner, cream, Vaseline
☐ Made schedule for tomorrow
☐ EFT tapping
☐ Hot bath +/- aromatherapy
☐ Mirror covered
☐ Time in nature
☐ Social engagement
☐ Drank water
☐ Supplements
☐ Exercise

I Learned Today:

_____

_____

_____

Sugar _____

Caffeine _____

Alcohol _____

Date _____

Mood _____   Calmness _____   Energy Level _____   Pulling _____

Gratitude: _____

_____

Affirmation:

_____

_____

☐ Positive log (this page)
☐ 4-8-8 breathing
☐ Mindful check-ins
☐ Hat, scarf or ponytail
☐ Mascara or false eyelashes
☐ Bandages or fake nails
☐ Gloves
☐ Fidget toys
☐ Sensory tools
☐ Meditation or relaxation
☐ Enough sleep
☐ Good food
☐ Yoga

☐ Positive self-talk
☐ Questioned thoughts
☐ Reviewed thought flashcards
☐ Conditioner, cream, Vaseline
☐ Made schedule for tomorrow
☐ EFT tapping
☐ Hot bath +/- aromatherapy
☐ Mirror covered
☐ Time in nature
☐ Social engagement
☐ Drank water
☐ Supplements
☐ Exercise

I Learned Today:

_____

_____

_____

Sugar _____

Caffeine _____

Alcohol _____

"You can have results or excuses. Not both."
- Arnold Schwarzenegger

Mood _____   Calmness _____   Energy Level _____   Pulling _____

Gratitude: _____

_____

Affirmation:

_____

_____

☐ Positive log (this page)
☐ 4-8-8 breathing
☐ Mindful check-ins
☐ Hat, scarf or ponytail
☐ Mascara or false eyelashes
☐ Bandages or fake nails
☐ Gloves
☐ Fidget toys
☐ Sensory tools
☐ Meditation or relaxation
☐ Enough sleep
☐ Good food
☐ Yoga

☐ Positive self-talk
☐ Questioned thoughts
☐ Reviewed thought flashcards
☐ Conditioner, cream, Vaseline
☐ Made schedule for tomorrow
☐ EFT tapping
☐ Hot bath +/- aromatherapy
☐ Mirror covered
☐ Time in nature
☐ Social engagement
☐ Drank water
☐ Supplements
☐ Exercise

I Learned Today:

_____

_____

_____

Sugar _____

Caffeine _____

Alcohol _____

Date _____

Mood _____   Calmness _____   Energy Level _____   Pulling _____

Gratitude: _____

_____

Affirmation:

_____

_____

☐ Positive log (this page)   ☐ Positive self-talk
☐ 4-8-8 breathing   ☐ Questioned thoughts
☐ Mindful check-ins   ☐ Reviewed thought flashcards
☐ Hat, scarf or ponytail   ☐ Conditioner, cream, Vaseline
☐ Mascara or false eyelashes   ☐ Made schedule for tomorrow
☐ Bandages or fake nails   ☐ EFT tapping
☐ Gloves   ☐ Hot bath +/- aromatherapy
☐ Fidget toys   ☐ Mirror covered
☐ Sensory tools   ☐ Time in nature
☐ Meditation or relaxation   ☐ Social engagement
☐ Enough sleep   ☐ Drank water
☐ Good food   ☐ Supplements
☐ Yoga   ☐ Exercise

I Learned Today:

_____

_____

_____

Sugar _____

Caffeine _____

Alcohol _____

"Although the world is full of suffering, it is also full of the overcoming of it."
- Helen Keller

Date _____

Mood _____   Calmness _____   Energy Level _____   Pulling _____

Gratitude: _____

_____

Affirmation:

_____

_____

- ☐ Positive log (this page)
- ☐ 4-8-8 breathing
- ☐ Mindful check-ins
- ☐ Hat, scarf or ponytail
- ☐ Mascara or false eyelashes
- ☐ Bandages or fake nails
- ☐ Gloves
- ☐ Fidget toys
- ☐ Sensory tools
- ☐ Meditation or relaxation
- ☐ Enough sleep
- ☐ Good food
- ☐ Yoga

- ☐ Positive self-talk
- ☐ Questioned thoughts
- ☐ Reviewed thought flashcards
- ☐ Conditioner, cream, Vaseline
- ☐ Made schedule for tomorrow
- ☐ EFT tapping
- ☐ Hot bath +/- aromatherapy
- ☐ Mirror covered
- ☐ Time in nature
- ☐ Social engagement
- ☐ Drank water
- ☐ Supplements
- ☐ Exercise

Sugar	_____
Caffeine	_____
Alcohol	_____

I Learned Today:

_____

_____

_____

"It does not matter how slowly you go as long as you do not stop."
– Confucius

Date _____

Mood _____   Calmness _____   Energy Level _____   Pulling _____

Gratitude: _____

_____

Affirmation:

_____

_____

☐ Positive log (this page)   ☐ Positive self-talk
☐ 4-8-8 breathing   ☐ Questioned thoughts
☐ Mindful check-ins   ☐ Reviewed thought flashcards
☐ Hat, scarf or ponytail   ☐ Conditioner, cream, Vaseline
☐ Mascara or false eyelashes   ☐ Made schedule for tomorrow
☐ Bandages or fake nails   ☐ EFT tapping
☐ Gloves   ☐ Hot bath +/- aromatherapy
☐ Fidget toys   ☐ Mirror covered
☐ Sensory tools   ☐ Time in nature
☐ Meditation or relaxation   ☐ Social engagement
☐ Enough sleep   ☐ Drank water
☐ Good food   ☐ Supplements
☐ Yoga   ☐ Exercise

I Learned Today:

_____

_____

_____

Sugar _____

Caffeine _____

Alcohol _____

"The difference between winning and losing is most often not quitting."
- Walt Disney

Date _____

Mood _____   Calmness _____   Energy Level _____   Pulling _____

Gratitude: _____

_____

Affirmation:

_____

_____

☐ Positive log (this page)   ☐ Positive self-talk
☐ 4-8-8 breathing   ☐ Questioned thoughts
☐ Mindful check-ins   ☐ Reviewed thought flashcards
☐ Hat, scarf or ponytail   ☐ Conditioner, cream, Vaseline
☐ Mascara or false eyelashes   ☐ Made schedule for tomorrow
☐ Bandages or fake nails   ☐ EFT tapping
☐ Gloves   ☐ Hot bath +/- aromatherapy
☐ Fidget toys   ☐ Mirror covered
☐ Sensory tools   ☐ Time in nature
☐ Meditation or relaxation   ☐ Social engagement
☐ Enough sleep   ☐ Drank water
☐ Good food   ☐ Supplements
☐ Yoga   ☐ Exercise

I Learned Today:

_____

_____

_____

Sugar _____

Caffeine _____

Alcohol _____

"You must expect great things of yourself before you can do them."
- Michael Jordan

Date _____

Mood _____   Calmness _____   Energy Level _____   Pulling _____

Gratitude: _____
_____

Affirmation:
_____
_____

- [ ] Positive log (this page)
- [ ] 4-8-8 breathing
- [ ] Mindful check-ins
- [ ] Hat, scarf or ponytail
- [ ] Mascara or false eyelashes
- [ ] Bandages or fake nails
- [ ] Gloves
- [ ] Fidget toys
- [ ] Sensory tools
- [ ] Meditation or relaxation
- [ ] Enough sleep
- [ ] Good food
- [ ] Yoga

- [ ] Positive self-talk
- [ ] Questioned thoughts
- [ ] Reviewed thought flashcards
- [ ] Conditioner, cream, Vaseline
- [ ] Made schedule for tomorrow
- [ ] EFT tapping
- [ ] Hot bath +/- aromatherapy
- [ ] Mirror covered
- [ ] Time in nature
- [ ] Social engagement
- [ ] Drank water
- [ ] Supplements
- [ ] Exercise

I Learned Today:
_____
_____
_____

Sugar _____

Caffeine _____

Alcohol _____

"You take your life in your own hands, and what happens? A terrible thing, no one to blame."
– Erica Jong

Date _____

Mood ____   Calmness ____   Energy Level ____   Pulling ____

Gratitude: _____

_____

Affirmation:

_____

_____

- ☐ Positive log (this page)
- ☐ 4-8-8 breathing
- ☐ Mindful check-ins
- ☐ Hat, scarf or ponytail
- ☐ Mascara or false eyelashes
- ☐ Bandages or fake nails
- ☐ Gloves
- ☐ Fidget toys
- ☐ Sensory tools
- ☐ Meditation or relaxation
- ☐ Enough sleep
- ☐ Good food
- ☐ Yoga

- ☐ Positive self-talk
- ☐ Questioned thoughts
- ☐ Reviewed thought flashcards
- ☐ Conditioner, cream, Vaseline
- ☐ Made schedule for tomorrow
- ☐ EFT tapping
- ☐ Hot bath +/- aromatherapy
- ☐ Mirror covered
- ☐ Time in nature
- ☐ Social engagement
- ☐ Drank water
- ☐ Supplements
- ☐ Exercise

Sugar _____

Caffeine _____

Alcohol _____

I Learned Today:

_____

_____

_____

"Be faithful in small things because it is in them that your faith lies."
- Mother Teresa

Date _____

Mood _____   Calmness _____   Energy Level _____   Pulling _____

Gratitude: _____

_____

Affirmation:

_____

_____

☐ Positive log (this page)   ☐ Positive self-talk
☐ 4-8-8 breathing   ☐ Questioned thoughts
☐ Mindful check-ins   ☐ Reviewed thought flashcards
☐ Hat, scarf or ponytail   ☐ Conditioner, cream, Vaseline
☐ Mascara or false eyelashes   ☐ Made schedule for tomorrow
☐ Bandages or fake nails   ☐ EFT tapping
☐ Gloves   ☐ Hot bath +/- aromatherapy
☐ Fidget toys   ☐ Mirror covered
☐ Sensory tools   ☐ Time in nature
☐ Meditation or relaxation   ☐ Social engagement
☐ Enough sleep   ☐ Drank water
☐ Good food   ☐ Supplements
☐ Yoga   ☐ Exercise

I Learned Today:

_____

_____

_____

Sugar _____

Caffeine _____

Alcohol _____

"The temptation to quit will be greatest just before you are about to succeed."
- Chinese Proverb

Date _____

Mood _____   Calmness _____   Energy Level _____   Pulling _____

Gratitude: _____

_____

Affirmation:

_____

_____

☐ Positive log (this page)   ☐ Positive self-talk
☐ 4-8-8 breathing   ☐ Questioned thoughts
☐ Mindful check-ins   ☐ Reviewed thought flashcards
☐ Hat, scarf or ponytail   ☐ Conditioner, cream, Vaseline
☐ Mascara or false eyelashes   ☐ Made schedule for tomorrow
☐ Bandages or fake nails   ☐ EFT tapping
☐ Gloves   ☐ Hot bath +/- aromatherapy
☐ Fidget toys   ☐ Mirror covered
☐ Sensory tools   ☐ Time in nature
☐ Meditation or relaxation   ☐ Social engagement
☐ Enough sleep   ☐ Drank water
☐ Good food   ☐ Supplements
☐ Yoga   ☐ Exercise

I Learned Today:

_____

_____

_____

Sugar	_____
Caffeine	_____
Alcohol	_____

"Remember, we all stumble, every one of us. That's why it's a comfort to go hand in hand."
- Emily Kimbrough

Date _____

Mood ____   Calmness ____   Energy Level ____   Pulling ____

Gratitude:

_____

_____

Affirmation:

_____

_____

- [ ] Positive log (this page)
- [ ] 4-8-8 breathing
- [ ] Mindful check-ins
- [ ] Hat, scarf or ponytail
- [ ] Mascara or false eyelashes
- [ ] Bandages or fake nails
- [ ] Gloves
- [ ] Fidget toys
- [ ] Sensory tools
- [ ] Meditation or relaxation
- [ ] Enough sleep
- [ ] Good food
- [ ] Yoga

- [ ] Positive self-talk
- [ ] Questioned thoughts
- [ ] Reviewed thought flashcards
- [ ] Conditioner, cream, Vaseline
- [ ] Made schedule for tomorrow
- [ ] EFT tapping
- [ ] Hot bath +/- aromatherapy
- [ ] Mirror covered
- [ ] Time in nature
- [ ] Social engagement
- [ ] Drank water
- [ ] Supplements
- [ ] Exercise

I Learned Today:

_____

_____

_____

Sugar _____

Caffeine _____

Alcohol _____

"Keep your face to the sunshine and you can never see the shadow."
- Helen Keller

Date _____

Mood ____ Calmness ____ Energy Level ____ Pulling ____

Gratitude: _____

_____

Affirmation:

_____

_____

- ☐ Positive log (this page)
- ☐ 4-8-8 breathing
- ☐ Mindful check-ins
- ☐ Hat, scarf or ponytail
- ☐ Mascara or false eyelashes
- ☐ Bandages or fake nails
- ☐ Gloves
- ☐ Fidget toys
- ☐ Sensory tools
- ☐ Meditation or relaxation
- ☐ Enough sleep
- ☐ Good food
- ☐ Yoga

- ☐ Positive self-talk
- ☐ Questioned thoughts
- ☐ Reviewed thought flashcards
- ☐ Conditioner, cream, Vaseline
- ☐ Made schedule for tomorrow
- ☐ EFT tapping
- ☐ Hot bath +/- aromatherapy
- ☐ Mirror covered
- ☐ Time in nature
- ☐ Social engagement
- ☐ Drank water
- ☐ Supplements
- ☐ Exercise

I Learned Today:

_____

_____

_____

Sugar _____

Caffeine _____

Alcohol _____

"The most common way people give up their power is by thinking they don't have any." – Alice Walker

Date _____

Mood _____ Calmness _____ Energy Level _____ Pulling _____

Gratitude: _____

_____

Affirmation:

_____

_____

☐ Positive log (this page)   ☐ Positive self-talk
☐ 4-8-8 breathing   ☐ Questioned thoughts
☐ Mindful check-ins   ☐ Reviewed thought flashcards
☐ Hat, scarf or ponytail   ☐ Conditioner, cream, Vaseline
☐ Mascara or false eyelashes   ☐ Made schedule for tomorrow
☐ Bandages or fake nails   ☐ EFT tapping
☐ Gloves   ☐ Hot bath +/- aromatherapy
☐ Fidget toys   ☐ Mirror covered
☐ Sensory tools   ☐ Time in nature
☐ Meditation or relaxation   ☐ Social engagement
☐ Enough sleep   ☐ Drank water
☐ Good food   ☐ Supplements
☐ Yoga   ☐ Exercise

I Learned Today:

_____

_____

_____

Sugar _____

Caffeine _____

Alcohol _____

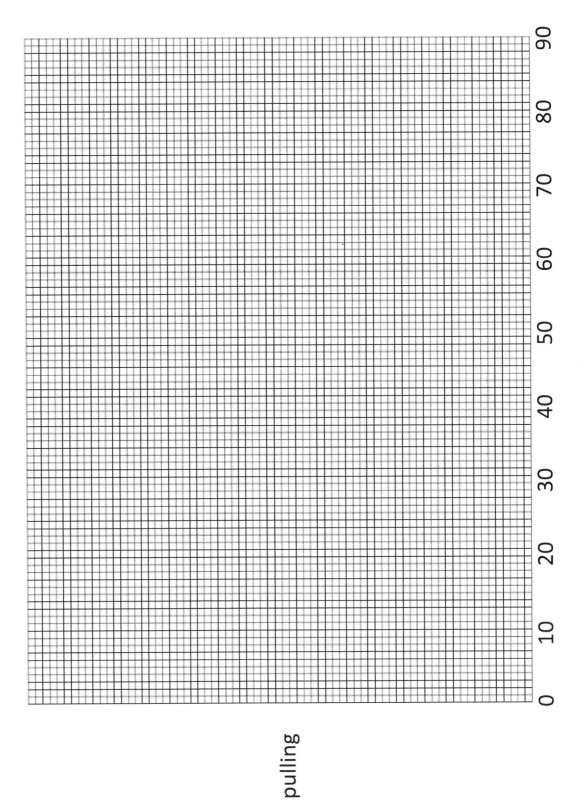

pulling

day

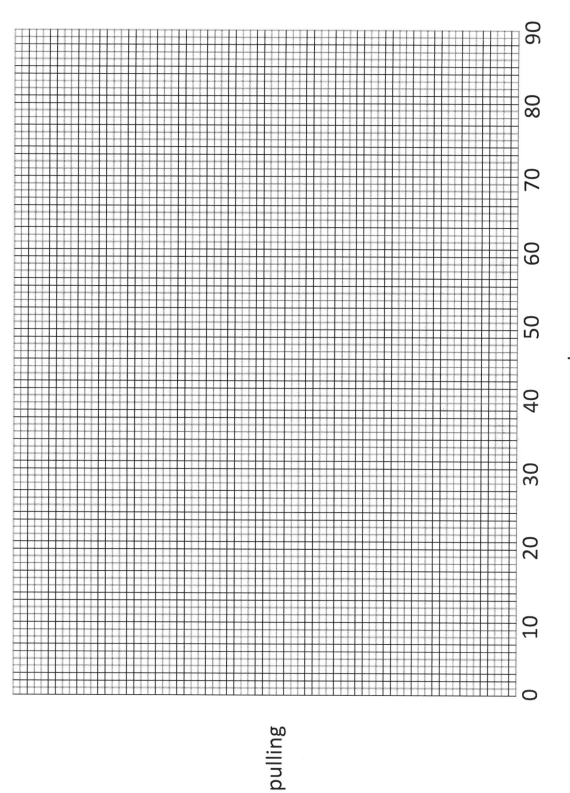

pulling

day

Acknowledgments

Thank you to my coaching clients for helping me realize that what I call the "positive log" in my book, "Skin Picking" is indeed the key daily accountability strategy, and especially to Katie J. for recognizing that a checklist is an easier method to positive logging.

Thank you to Julie Mann for planting the seed in my head to create a journal.

Thank you to Nicholas DeSomov for being a stellar husband and also for the cover design.

About the Author:

Annette Pasternak, Ph.D., also known as the "Stop Skin Picking Coach," is a certified holistic health coach, practitioner of functional diagnostic nutrition (FDN), and is the author of "Skin Picking: The Freedom to Finally Stop." Formerly a research scientist, college professor and high school chemistry teacher who struggled for more than two decades with chronic skin picking, Annette now coaches others around the world to break free from its tenacious grip. She also has an online course for self-help available at breakfreefromskinpicking.com.
Contact Annette through her website at www.stopskinpickingcoach.com.

Made in the USA
San Bernardino, CA
05 March 2017